F

Plante, David.
The foreigner.

Books by David Plante

The Foreigner

David Plante

THE
FOREIGNER

ATHENEUM
New York
1984

Portions of this book have previously appeared in *The New Yorker*.
I wish to thank the John Simon Guggenheim Foundation for its support.

Library of Congress Cataloging in Publication Data

Plante, David.
   The foreigner.

     1. Spain—History—Civil War, 1936–1939—Fiction.
I. Title.
PS3566.L257F6 1984   813'.54   —   84–45039
ISBN 0–689–11491–5

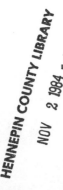

Copyright © 1984 by David Plante
All rights reserved
Composition by Heritage Printers, Inc., Charlotte, North Carolina
Manufactured by Fairfield Graphics, Fairfield, Pennsylvania
Designed by Harry Ford
First Edition

For Catharine Carver

"In Spain you could not tell about anything."
Ernest Hemingway

Part One

I

I wᴀs brought up in two countries.
The outer country, vast, was America.

I belonged to another, a small one within the large: the French parish, in Providence, Rhode Island, into which I was born.

The small French parish had no rights in America, which really had rights over me.

I was frightened of America, and one day, all by myself, I tore up the American flag.

I was also frightened of the French Church, so frightened I knew I would have condemned myself if I had dared desecrate any of its dark totems: a missal, a rosary, a sheaf of blessed palm.

These objects of the French Church could save me only within myself. I had to concentrate on them while I prayed. American objects exposed me to a dangerous outside which demanded my attention whether I liked it or not. I had no faith in what was outside, and I couldn't in any way fix on the American flag to pray. But America, whether I liked it or not, would take me out of myself, to where there was no salvation, and destroy me.

Trying to fantasize what it would be to live in another country, I'd stop myself and think: you phony.

Whenever I was asked by friends in college what my nationality was, I would answer, "French." On all the forms I had to fill out, whenever I saw *Nationality*, I would write *French*. It meant blood, but "French" did not mean "coming from France." In the parish, France, as a country, was hardly referred to, and I had no more sense of it than I had of England or Italy or Spain. It belonged, with those other countries, to Europe. My parents had no idea when their ancestors left from France for Canada, or from what part. One of my aunts mentioned a great great aunt who arrived in Quebec possessing only a pair of lace gloves and an ivory fan, and that was all we knew. France, that distant country, was not our old country.

We came from French Canada, and at the beginning of every day in the parish school, we sang, "Ô Canada, terre de nos aïeux."

I was never curious about French Canada.

I was curious about France.

During the Easter break of my freshman year, I flew to Chicago with my roommate, invited by his family. Charlie told his parents that I could speak French, that I was "French." Their eyes opened, and I, surprised, realized that to speak French, to claim French blood, was, in the middle vastness of America, to have distinction. I wanted to be sincere, but I regretted telling them I was Canuck and explaining what a Canuck was, because I liked the special interest they had in my being, as they'd thought, *of* France.

Charlie lived in Oak Park, on North Kenilworth Avenue, across from the house where Ernest Hemingway was brought up, and from which, perhaps, he had left to go to Europe for the first time.

Charlie wanted to be a painter; he said, laughing, he would one day go to Paris and be a painter.

I thought he was taking the big risk of being a phony.

Back in Providence and Boston, I developed a vivid expectation of what France might be like from what I imagined no one from the parish could appreciate: paintings. In the cities' museums, I went from room to room studying the French painters, and in their pictures I glimpsed marble topped café tables with green bottles, fans and opera glasses on the red velvet elbow rests of opera boxes, apples on a rucked tablecloth, a ballet slipper and a pink sash. There were, too, lines of poplar trees, bridges over streams, church steeples rising above multi-angled roofs, and bulging haystacks colored in different pictures by blue to red phases of sunlight.

I was more aware of things in these pictures than I was of what appeared in the kitchen at supper on the bare Formica table at which my parents and my brothers and I silently ate: the bottle of milk, the jam glasses, the mismatched plates and knives and forks and spoons heaped to one side, the loaf of cellophane-wrapped bread, the bowls of mashed potatoes and canned string beans, the cracked platter of pork sausages, and the boudin, a black blood pudding which only my parents ate.

An American took me into Europe. After oysters and cold white wine with Hemingway, I walked with him along fresh washed gravel paths by fountains blowing in the bright light.

He'd liked the French painters. He'd studied them in Paris when he was hungry and his hunger made the lines

5

and colors clear and sharp. He'd learned from them; what he learned was, he said, "a secret."

Hemingway was an authority of Europe; because of what he knew, I didn't question his right to be there. I couldn't imagine him arriving by boat, not knowing about the streets, museums, cafés, and not speaking the languages; he seemed to have known Europe all his life. He could, in Paris, order a drink I had never heard of, a "fine," and drink it with the familiarity of someone who had drunk "fines" all his life. He knew what cafés to go to, what restaurants, what dancings; he knew what to say to taxi drivers and waiters and prostitutes, in their argot. It was especially in his descriptions—the paddock under the new leafed tree, the pink racing paper—that I sensed the certainty of his possession of Europe.

He had a right to live in Europe, an American who had made another country his own. In Europe, he could even sin, and simply because he was there he was justified in his sinning. I, in America, was an unjustified sinner.

He was what I wanted to be, but would have to risk everything to become: a foreigner.

Though I lived outside the parish now, a boarder at Boston College, I remained, in myself, parochial; that is, my life was centered on my private thoughts and feelings. My roommate Charlie ran for Freshman Class President and won, and it occurred to me that I would never have thought of becoming president. I had no idea what a president did, and I had no interest in the college as a social institution. Civic duty was demanded of me, and never originated with me. But I was pleased that Charlie, who everyone knew was my roommate, was president.

He would make me go out to dances with him to the Catholic girls' colleges.

When I introduced him to girls I met at the hops, I said, "This is Charlie, the class president, my roommate."

My freshman year, I was in ROTC, training to be an officer in my country's army. I did not like it; America was no longer fighting a war, and I did not believe the army should be able to induct me, though I knew that one day it would whether I liked it or not. I quit ROTC in my Sophomore year. But the rights of my country to take me back into the army whenever it wished were absolute, and, at eighteen when I had to register for the draft, America was, to me, the army, in which I must fulfill my duty as a soldier.

My only way out was to be a foreigner in another country.

I knew very little about Europe. The pictures in the museums were windows, but I could not lean in and see what streets the café drinkers and ballet dancers went down on their ways home, or what lay beyond the paths across the fields and the narrow canals. I thought that if I could I would see the destruction of World War II. Around the corners of the pictures were the ruins of houses, the trenches and blasted trees. Everywhere, outside of my sight, were the armies. The armies had destroyed millions. It was as if Europe had gone beyond everything I could fear, or imagine.

The deep, dark war in Europe caused in me a strange longing to be there.

On a weekend back in the parish, I told my parents, at supper, that I'd decided to go abroad to study for a year. I didn't ask them; I told them. They didn't object. If anyone could have, it would have been my brother Albert, who was giving me the money to go to college; my parents could not

7

have afforded it. After I told them, we finished our supper in silence. I wrote to my brother and told him my plans; he wrote back that of course I should go.

He was a major in the Marine Corps. He'd joined the Marines when he was sixteen, and fought the Japanese in the South Pacific in World War II. I could not imagine him ever having fought. He never talked about it. But whenever I thought about him, he was wearing his officer's uniform. He'd never been to Europe. In his letter he said I must, in Europe, feel free. I must do what he had never been able to do. He suggested I grow a beard, and I thought: I'm more original than that.

I sent off my application for the study program and a check, and I went each day to my mailbox, anxious. I'd made a choice, but I wasn't sure I'd be allowed to fulfill the choice. I found, one morning, an envelope from the program, and as I opened the end I saw, in the folded letter, my check. Charlie was with me. I said, "They've turned down my application." I couldn't make myself read the letter. Charlie, who always tore open his letters, said, "Give it to me." He read the letter and told me, "They've returned the check because you didn't sign it. You've been accepted. Why did you think they wouldn't?" There was no reason why I shouldn't have been accepted, but it had seemed to me that the powers upon which my acceptance depended would of course reject me. I despised this expectation in myself.

By going to Europe I would begin a new life in which the choices would be up to me and the fulfillment of the choices would be up to me.

To get my passport I had to swear I was not a Communist. As the Jesuits at Boston College had taught me, I made a mental reservation: I was not going to swear to being, or not being, anything but what I wanted to be or not be, and no one was going to force me. In the office in the City Hall, I raised my hand and moved my lips, but I did not utter any words.

In Boston, I went to the French Consul for a visa. Filling out the application form, where it said "Nationalité" I wrote, as I always had, "French." The secretary said, "But if you're French you don't need a visa." I simply looked at her. She asked, "Where were you born?" "In America," I said. "Then," she said, "you're American."

For my French visa a medical examination was required. I did not want one. I had never, in my recollection, had one. After I made an appointment with the parish doctor, I felt I had condemned myself. We, as a family, hardly knew the doctor, for my parents did not take us to him for checkups, and he was asked to the house only reluctantly when we children had measles or mumps. It seemed to us that when we saw him he might tell us we were going to die. My terror was that he would ask me to undress and would touch my body. As the day came, I imagined, more and more acutely, his touching my exposed body. The night before, I couldn't sleep; I got up and sat in the kitchen, condemned. I knew that if I didn't have the physical I couldn't go to Europe, though I wasn't sure why I must have it: perhaps because there was fear in Europe that I would come with a diseased body. I must submit that body to the authorities. On the table I left a note for my parents: I am not going to the doctor's. In bed again, I couldn't sleep. In the early morning, I heard, from the kitchen, my parents talking; I knew they were talking about me. My father left for work and my mother came into my room and said, quietly,

"It's time for you to get ready for the doctor, if you want to go." I said nothing, but, as if it were demanded of me, got up, got ready, and walked to the doctor's small, dim office, which was across from the church. He asked me only to unbutton my shirt so he could put the stethoscope to my chest.

I received my visa, stamped in my passport, by registered mail.

With very little money, I went to a department store in downtown Providence to buy clothes which I thought would be right for Europe: light colored trousers and a vividly striped jacket and a more vividly striped vest.

As I packed, my parents left me alone.

All my father said was, "Sois sage, tsi gars, là bas."

My great risk in going abroad was this: being a phony. As there was no way out of my affectation, I would have to risk it.

My brothers gave me going away gifts: a camera, a bottle of after shave lotion, a little leather case with nail clip and file. One of my sisters-in-law gave me a narrow black binder with loose leaves for, she said, keeping a diary while I was "overseas."

With a very big plaid suitcase, I boarded the train for New York. My parents came to stand on the platform to see me off, as did some of my brothers. I did not wave from the window, but simply held my hand up and smiled; they held up their hands, and they looked, I thought, sad. Like a black and white photograph, they slid from view. I felt my chest heave, but I held my breath. I sat back in my seat.

A girl next to me, my age, asked, "Where're you going?"

"Europe," I said.

She wanted to go to Europe.

I was nineteen.

In Pennsylvania Station, beneath high, dark arches, I sat on a bench and waited for a dorm mate from college, Joe, to meet me, and while I waited I began my diary: June 8, 1959. I spent two days with Joe at his home in New Jersey.

We saw two other friends from college, Chris and Harry, who were staying in a hotel in New York; because I had decided to go to Europe, they decided to go over, too, for the summer when I would be free to do what I wanted before I started classes in Paris in the fall. They had money, and were flying; I didn't have money, and was going by boat. The three friends came to the dock with me.

As I was climbing the gang plank of the Liberté, I saw, standing to the side at the top, my brother Albert. He was in his major's uniform. I ran up, but in front of him put my suitcase down and kept my arms to my sides, and he stood back and put his hands on my shoulders.

"Don't worry about anything while you're there," he said, "even if it's upsetting."

His highly polished military shoes shone. Albert said he had located my cabin, thinking he might have found me there, and I and my college friends followed him down shining stairs, along shining corridors, into a small hot cabin lit by a pale blue bulb. All the signs were in French; I did not understand them all, but suddenly French appeared to me a strange language. I wanted to discover the ship, deciphering all the signs, by myself.

Joe had got me to the ship late, and there were announcements that visitors should disembark. At the rail, I stood with the hundreds of other passengers, all of us waving; many passengers threw out streamers, red, blue, green, yellow, and band music blasted from loudspeakers. When the ship moved, it was as if suddenly, unexpectedly. I saw the looped streamers tighten, and everyone shouted more and waved with both arms, myself included. I had to think of something, feel something quickly, quickly, before it was too late—think it, feel it, and remember it—but, taken in by some powerful force pulling away from the dock, I thought and felt nothing, and watched the streamers snap and trail down the sides of the dock and ship. There remained, for a moment, the sense that the ship was using all its force to pull away from the edge of the continent, which drew it back with an almost equal force; and then it broke away, and very soon I was seeing the whole of the dock, and could no longer make out Albert and my friends.

I remained at the rail and watched the skyscrapers sink.

2

I KEPT getting lost in the corridors. When I found my cabin again, I also found a young man in it unpacking, my cabin mate. I introduced myself to him, and thought: he doesn't know anything about me, and, on the ship, can't know anything about me but what I tell him.

He asked me if I'd put my name down for a sitting, which I didn't understand; he explained, and said it might be too late for the second sitting, which everyone wanted, so I'd better hurry. The second sitting was all booked up, and I was put down for the first. A steward in a starched white jacket and black and gold epaulettes asked me, in French, if I wanted to sit at a French or English speaking table, and I said, "French."

Out on deck, I walked under the lifeboats; the deck was crowded, and in a group of people at the stern I saw my cabin mate. I went to him, and he introduced me to others. I was in my striped jacket. When other people came along, I introduced myself. We swayed with the slow up and down movement of the ship. The introductory question was, "Is this your first trip to Europe?" Some people answered, "Oh no," and the ones for whom it was the first trip looked at these with a kind of awe, and, too, a kind of suspicion. The ones who had been before tried to tell the ones who hadn't what to expect over there. I thought: I'm not going to listen. A steward, without epaulettes, came out on deck ringing a small, hand held xylophone.

In the salle à manger, I sat among French people. We all nodded at one another. Across from me sat a middle-aged woman with a big bosom. She was between her two daughters, without bosoms. She, spreading her napkin across her lap, spoke to me in French, too rapid for me to understand; I leaned towards her, and she asked me, in English, "Is this your first voyage to France?" "Oh yes," I said. Her daughters spoke English, too, as did most people at the table. They spoke to me in English, and I spoke to them in hesitant French.

Big bosomed Madame said to me, "Vous avez un accent Canadien."

"Oui," I said.

"Comment ça c'fait?"

I went hot. I said, "Je suis Canadien-Français."

"Ah," she said.

Waiters came along with bright salvers from which, with a fork and knife, they placed a little, lightly browned rectangle on each plate: brains. I had never eaten brains. I ate the brains. Another waiter poured out wine.

Madame told me she had been in French Canada for five years. She had had enough of it; she'd found it impossible. For example, when she told them she was returning to France, the French Canadians had asked her, "Will you go by car or train?" Madame pursed her lips. "Impossible," she said.

I'd better speak to her in English, I thought.

14

None of the food served had I ever eaten before. It was all French cooking.

Madame was friendly; her two daughters smiled at me from time to time.

With cheese at the end of the meal there was fruit. I picked a small bunch of grapes from the bowl and, as I was about to put a grape into my mouth, Madame stopped me. She held up her hands. "Ah non, Monsieur," she said; "les raisins ne sont pas propres." She filled my water glass with water, took the bunch of grapes from my hand, and plunged it up and down in the glass, from which the water splashed onto the white tablecloth; then she held the bunch out to me by its stem, gleaming, and I took it. Wet, yellow, it continued to gleam on my plate. I was a little drunk. I stared at the grapes as if they had appeared there, in space. My awareness was itself a white space in which the grapes on the plate, the cups, the spoons, the glasses of brandy, the cigarettes in the glass ashtrays, the hands over the long table, the leaning heads, all multiplied in the tinted mirrors of the dining room, were objects of my joy. I had never seen anything.

After dinner, I went out to walk the vibrating deck, and I imagined that, not the nighttime illuminations, but the vibrations gave off the thin surfaces of light. Unable to walk steadily, I stayed close to the rail, and whenever the ship seemed to me to shift course and go sideways I held on. I imagined myself on a ship that stood out in curved, riveted, shining white planes on a white ocean.

Everything made me happy, even the canvas chairs folded up and tied together, one left open, a lap rug thrown over it, and by it on the deck an empty consommé cup.

I went to the lounge where I sat at tables with people I'd

met, and where I met others. We drank. The lounge became crowded when the second sitting finished seating. A band came in and played, and I asked one of the young women at a table to dance. I did not want to become attached to anyone in particular; I danced with different young women, and sometimes with older women.

I wanted to supply everyone with evidence that I was a bright person, someone who could take any risk, and laugh.

Laughing, I would hear above my laughter, as from a great height, a voice say, "You fool."

At a table, I found myself talking to a middle-aged Belgian couple with a tall daughter. The man offered me a drink. When the band played, he suggested I might dance with his daughter. I did; she plodded. Back at the table, he and his wife smiled at me. I thought: they believe I'm a nice boy. I remained at their table.

I looked about the lounge, at the piano on the abandoned platform, the empty dance floor, the small, round, cloth covered tables, the passengers, and, at the table just to the side of me, a young black woman.

The moment I saw her I looked about as if to see from others what to do, then turned back to her again. She was, it seemed to me, searching the lounge for someone. She was wearing a strapless evening dress, and her narrow, hunched black shoulders and back gleamed. Her neck was long and her short stiff hair revealed the nape. She kept glancing about the lounge, and I saw, as she glanced towards me, her large white eyes. I saw, too, her clavicle, and the upper parts of her black breasts. She rubbed her nose with the knuckle of a long bent finger, and turned away.

The parquet dance floor was spread with a canvas sheet marked with numbered squares, and stewards in white jackets moved horses on wooden stands from one square to another as a steward to the side called out numbers; at their table, the players kept scores on cards, and sometimes someone groaned, or someone cheered. The black woman didn't play, but looked attentively; she bit her upper lip, released it, and bit her lower lip.

She sat up, arching her finely boned back, and stretched out her slender arms so the black hollows under her arms showed. She yawned, then got up and left the lounge.

After a while, I excused myself and got up and went out. I sauntered all around to the other side of the ship, and went in. At the entrance to the lounge I watched, over the heads of people sitting, dancers on the dance floor; they were in blue light. At a corner table was the black woman; in the light, her skin had a blue sheen to it. People at the intervening tables pulled in their chairs to let me pass. I stood at her table, and she blinked up at me; there were flecks of black in the whites of her eyes. She raised a pale palm crisscrossed with black lines.

I had never been close to a black person.

Dancing, I swung her one way, then the other, then swung her round. Her face tilted in many different directions. She didn't look at me, but at others dancing about us. Under my hand I felt the cloth of her dress slide against her body. I was sure that she was unaware of me; but I was very aware of myself. Swinging her, I lost balance and she lurched; bent over, she laughed, and put a hand, the long fine fingers bent at various angles, to her mouth and laughed more, her white teeth and black gums showing through her fingers. Holding her, not sure why she was laughing, I made myself laugh too. The other couples danced around us. Then the black woman righted herself, stood back from me, and, about to leave me I thought, she took my hand and led me off the dance floor to her table.

Wanting her to think I knew just what to do, I signalled the waiter. The waiter didn't come. I had to raise my arm higher. When he came I thought she would see that I knew what to do when I pointed, on the table before her, to a tall glass with melting crushed ice and a diluted green liquid in its bottom. I ordered two. Ordering, I thought: I can do anything. I sat back and searched the lounge as the black woman did. It was as if I had made a choice, and I wanted everyone to see that I had.

When the drinks came she picked one up as if the one she had finished refilled itself, and, her eyes still searching from right to left, sipped through the straw. She was overly attentive to what was going on about her, and whenever, at other tables, someone made a sharp movement, she turned to the table, the straw stuck delicately to her large lower lip, and stared.

By the entrance of the lounge I noticed a dark young man who was smiling at me; he made a sign and I, startled, was rising from my chair when I saw that he was signalling to the black woman, who got up and went to him. Her body was sparking at the shoulders, at the shoulder blades, at her finger tips, as if with the imminent realization of what she had been anticipating. As she approached him, the man turned away, and she slipped in between him and the wall, so I saw her facial twitches and frowns. As the man spoke she pouted. She spoke only briefly, and the man went away. I recognized him: he played the saxophone in the band. I thought she would not come back to me, but go to another table, or go out. She came back.

The smiling man from the band came into the lounge again and stood by the door. From her purse, the woman took a cigarette; I reached for matches by the ashtray and lit the cigarette for her. She held it between the long fingers of a limp hand, bent downwards at the wrist. After three puffs she stubbed the cigarette out. She raised her hand to the man, who came over, his heavy hips gyrating about the tables. Smiling, he leaned, as if bowing.

In French, she said, "I can't do it."

He continued to smile, but the corners of his eyes narrowed. He answered in French. "Very well, very well."

"I'm sorry," she said, "but I can't. I've thought about it. I can't."

Bowing still, he repeated, "Very well."

"I really can't," she said.

He left.

In a low voice, she said to me, "I'm Angela."

"Angela what?" I asked.

Her voice went lower. "Angela Johnson," she said.

Three tables from us, I saw the Belgian family at their table, their backs to me, and I thought: you see, I'm not nice, but different from what you thought.

Angela asked me, "Is this your first trip abroad?"

"Yes," I said.

Then she told me about Europe. She'd been before, many times. She'd lived in Europe for long periods. She told me how, in Europe, she had married and divorced, had had many affairs, and had tried to kill herself. She really liked Europe, and was going back, after a short stay in America, for good; she hated America.

Angela said, "I've got to have everything strange."

"So do I," I said.

She spoke as though she were carefully eliminating slang, or even idiom, from her talk; she had the fine, clear voice of a little girl trying to speak like an adult. I said to myself, Angela is a total phony. She sometimes angled her words with different, foreign accents. She wanted to be a foreigner. This was an affectation. At the risk of being as phony as she, I said, "I really want to get to know Paris, I want to discover those—," and here I felt a blush rise to my face for what I was about to say. Her lids half lowered, she said, "I know them all."

Abruptly, she stopped talking and looked at me as if she wondered who I was. She then said she was tired, and she left me to go down to her cabin.

I went down at dawn.

I woke up in the dim blue light when I heard the xylophone announcing breakfast. My cabin mate had not slept in his berth. After breakfast, I saw him with a woman, side by side in deck chairs, and I joined them. She was an older French woman, and she was, she told me, divorced. I wanted to get to know a divorced woman, but my cabin mate gave me a look which I understood to mean he wanted to be alone with her.

In the evening, they invited me to sit with them in the lounge. I looked about for Angela. When my cabin mate went to the bar for drinks, the French woman leaned towards me and asked, in French, "What shall I do with him? You see, I'm recently divorced from an American, and I don't want to become involved with another American." Her eyes were large and dark.

I said, "I'm sure he knows it's an exaggeration, your affaire de coeur."

She smiled. "Where did you learn that old fashioned expression?"

I was amazed that I had said what I'd said in French.

In a low voice, she said to me, "You don't seem American."

"Oh," I said.

"No, no, you don't. I think of you as French. It's in your blood."

I went red.

"And you're returning to France," she said.

"Returning?"

"Yes," she said "you are returning."

Angela didn't appear.

Over the days, I met many foreigners.

I did not write much in my diary, but when I did it was in a deck chair among other passengers. I met a Spanish girl in the next chair who was also keeping a diary. She said, "I don't write in it every day. I only write in what is most important to me." I thought, but everything is important.

I asked her about Spain.

Each day, the clock in the stairwell down to the cabins was put ahead an hour.

I looked for her every night, but it was not until the fourth night, late, that Angela appeared in the lounge. She sat at a table by herself; I wondered if she wanted to be alone, but I saw her look towards me and smile and raise her hand, and I went to her.

"Where've you been?" I asked.

"Here and there," she said.

"Oh."

She said, "If I were going to stay in Paris, I'd show you

Paris." She focused on me, and again it was as if, for a moment, she didn't know who I was. "Have you ever been to Barcelona?"

"No. I haven't ever."

"Well, I've seen all the places."

I asked, "Where else will you go in Europe if you don't stay in France?"

"Spain. I'm going to Barcelona."

"Why are you going there?"

It was as if I asked her a question with such an obvious answer, she seemed to wonder if there might be another reason for going she herself hadn't thought of. "What do you mean?"

"I was just wondering."

"You've never been to Barcelona?"

"No. I've never been."

"I've been to all the places," she said. She separated her legs, let her hands drop into her lap, and her body slumped. "I'm going to go back to Barcelona. I'm out of my mind. I shouldn't be going back, but I am." She might have been hit across the face, and her only reaction was to fall back into her chair. Then she sat up and laughed. "You want to know where I've been these past days?"

"Yes, I do."

She picked up a swizzle stick from the debris on the table, stood, and said, "Come on then," and I followed her out.

It seemed to me that if something had happened to her, it was to make her not care what she did; however exaggerated what she did, she'd dare anything because she didn't care.

The floors of the narrow, swaying corridors were shiny, and the doors to the cabins were reflected in them. There was in the silence a hiss from the overhead vents of rushing air. Angela and I moved quietly. At the end of a corridor we came to a wide metal door; she inserted a swizzle stick into a keyhole under a handle and leaned on the heavy door, which swung out and took her with it. She laughed and held it open for me. She knew where to go, along corridors now carpeted in blue, up wide stairs, and quickly into a large lounge. She took me by the arm and said softly, "We'll go to that table," and we passed among the tables to an empty one near the dance floor.

I kept thinking: we'll be found out.

Angela said, "Will you order me a drink?"

A waiter came when I raised a finger.

As she looked about, Angela's eyes became big and swelled a little; the round irises were completely visible in the white. She took in the men and women, and, it seemed, people who were invisible among the others; and I did the same. The invisible people became more and more numerous as the visible went out; tables were left empty, and yet, with glasses and napkins and even smoking cigarettes in ashtrays, they appeared to be crowded round by people. The band went out. The one remaining man at the bar buttoned his jacket and went out. Two waiters had stripped the tables of their cloths, and they waited for Angela and me to leave. I sat up as if to go, but Angela didn't move. She suddenly sat up; she raised her head, her eyes large, her ears sharp. Then she made small popping sounds with her lips and moved her shoulders, jiving, to the sound. She moved her arms, too, and softly snapped her fingers. She sank back, her arms crossed limply about her waist.

She said, "Let's go on deck."

I followed her out. When I opened the metal door, it

23

pulled me with it; she laughed, and I laughed. The deck rocked. As we walked under the suspended lifeboats we lurched from side to side, but I kept myself from bumping into her. From time to time we went to the rail and looked into the dark. White clouds formed at the sides of the ship and rose, in hissing foam, to the surface; the ship seemed to ride on these clouds. I held the rail; when she put her hand on the rail, I took mine off. We continued to walk. I walked at a distance from her. We didn't talk.

Then she said, "I'm going to Barcelona to see someone."

"A foreigner?" I asked, my voice suddenly high.

"An American."

She held her upper arms and hunched her shoulders against the cold.

I realized that I left it to her to say what we'd do or not do, that I would agree to anything she said.

"Maybe we should go back to our cabins," she said.

"All right."

She did not come to the Grande Soirée the evening before we docked.

Hot, entangled in paper streamers with others on the dance floor, when I saw a steward stoop to pick up a dropped glass and not smile, I felt removed from myself; but before the removed self could make a comment, I grabbed someone to hop with her in the crowd.

The next day I was woken by a knock on the door. I got up and looked through the crack, as the door was hooked open for air. The divorced woman told me to hurry. I found her on deck, looking over the water to a coast which appeared to be gleaming. She said, "Monsieur, je vous donne là France." She hugged me for a moment, then turned away. And I stared out.

As we docked at Le Havre, all my feelings and thoughts were uncoordinated in my excitement. I was standing among pieces of luggage stacked on the deck. Angela appeared, took me by the arm, and said, "Look, my friend would like you to do him a favor," and nodded towards a door where the saxophonist from the band was standing. "He'd like you to take something through customs." I drew back and asked, "What is it?" She shrugged. I thought, I can't do this. Then I thought, do it. I said, "All right." Angela went to speak to him, and he came to me with a flat, square, brown paper wrapped package. I put it in my suitcase. He told me he'd meet me in Paris, at the Gare St. Lazare. Angela disappeared, and, alone, I waited for the ship to dock.

My first detailed view of France was a concrete war bunker on a hill overlooking the sea. The long slits, from which I imagined artillery sticking out, were black; the cement was crumbling. I had a momentary sense that, in Europe, war was going on, and that people were being killed.

At a table set up on deck, just by the gangplank, my passport was stamped by an official with a round cap and a stiff visor. I turned away from the customs officer so he would have difficulty comparing my face with the photograph of my face. My suitcase was not looked into.

My feet struck the land as if I had expected the ground to be three or four inches higher, and the sudden small step into an unexpected depth threw me off balance.

Sweating, with my striped jacket and vest on, I followed other passengers, looking for someone I recognized. Among the moving crowd were porters in baggy blue overalls carrying big suitcases on straps over their shoulders; my suitcase, which I changed from hand to hand, bumped into people. I followed the crowd onto a rail platform where the boat train was waiting, and from one of the windows Angela waved to me. She had saved for me a window seat across from her.

In the compartment, I tried to retain all the details, as if everything might suddenly be taken away: the blue plush, the long narrow mirrors and photographs of the chateaux of France above the seats, the shiny brown walls, the luggage racks with string netting, the blue and white bulbs overhead, the heavy blue curtains with SNCF repeated in them, the shelf under the window, the metal ashtrays with flip tops on which SNCF was in relief. Everything—ventilator, coat hook, door latch—became an object of awareness, and there were too many objects to take in, too many to retain, too many to sustain in what I wanted to be a total awareness of France. I wanted to see, hear, touch, smell, taste everything, and be aware of everything I sensed, all together. There was a big black knob for Chauffage, and on the windowsill metal plaques on which were warnings, in three languages, not to lean out the window or throw any objects out.

I wanted to take France for granted; I wanted to know it all before I saw it. Now, when Angela said, "In France—," and then, as if already bored by it all, told me something that showed her familiarity with the place, I answered, "Yes, I know." But I did not know. While I listened to Angela, I stared out.

Framed by the window, I saw pictures. I saw church steeples among roofs, seen beyond long-lined fields; I saw poplar trees along both sides of straight roads, along river banks, in groves; I saw ponds with rowing boats among lily pads; saw old wooden bridges over canals, and barges in the canals, and locks; and, as the sun went down and set, I saw haystacks, great, bulging haystacks, change from yellow-brown to blue. Then, suddenly, I would find myself staring at a heap of broken bottles on a river bank, or beams leaning against the stone wall of a derelict house, or rusted oil drums in a field, and these broke up the pictures into uncomposed details, and a kind of panic would go through me, the panic of realizing I would never know what I came to know, would never possess what I came to possess; and the emergence, among the details, of another composition would reassure me that I could, that I already did, know Europe. Yet I stared, as if drawn to them, at the unexpected details: the smoking manure piles, the trees bare of branches way up their trunks.

Outside went dark.

Angela was sitting back in her seat, her black head lolling against the white antimacassar, her eyes closed. The lights in the compartment were lit. She opened her eyes and smiled at me. Her lips parted over her white teeth, and I suddenly thought: I am like Angela.

Then we came into the palely illuminated banlieue of Paris.

In the station, Angela signaled to a porter, who came into the compartment and passed her luggage out the window to another porter. I stood back. As she was leaving, she suddenly hugged me and kissed me, and I, silent, watched her go out, and watched her from the window follow the porter with her luggage through the crowded platform. I had perhaps imagined she would show me Europe; it was as if the strange promises of Europe were going with her, and I felt very much alone to find my own Europe. I watched till she disappeared among the disembarking passengers.

It had seemed to me, from a great distance, that all arrangements would take care of themselves once I arrived in Paris. I hadn't wanted arrangements made for me. Even as I lugged my suitcase along the platform, I didn't think, now I must find a place to sleep, but, now I'm in Paris.

At the barrier, the man from the band was waiting. He was wearing an American, short-sleeved, sport shirt, which hung out of his trousers. He came to help me with my case.

In the crowded, hot station I opened my case on the cement floor and gave him his package. He could not speak English well. He said, "I give you something." I didn't understand. "Quoi?" I asked. "Ah," he said, "vous parlez français." "Un peu," I said. He explained that he wanted to give me some money for having got his package through customs. I said, "Non, non, ce n'est pas nécessaire." I wanted to get away from him. He asked me where I was staying, and I thought I would lie to him, because I didn't want him to know I didn't have a place, didn't know Europe. I realized he had, in French, an accent, and I wondered what country he was from. I said, "I'm looking for a hotel." He said, "You come with me. You can stay where I stay." I had taken, at risk, his package through customs, but, now, I didn't want to risk any more. The station appeared high and dark. I said, "No." He said, "It is as you wish." His face was square and his eyes black, and I thought, he could do anything to you to get rid of you for doing what he wouldn't want anyone else to know you've done. Angela was familiar with the world he belonged to, and she hadn't got involved; had let me get involved perhaps to save herself. I wished Angela were with me, though I doubted she would have helped me (of course she wouldn't have helped

me). I said to the man, "Is it expensive, where you stay?"
He said, "No." I asked, "Where is it?" He could have said,
in hell, and I would have thought that an area of Paris. He
said, "Le Quinzième." I didn't know what that meant. "Very
well," I said. His package under one arm, he carried my
case with his free hand out of the station, where he hailed
a taxi. The air was hot and close and smelled of coal dust.
He took care of my suitcase, opened the taxi door for me,
and sat beside me in the back.

3

FROM the taxi window I saw trees and buildings made of light. We went about a wide square, in which were gushing fountains of light, and, beyond, a triumphal arch of light, and beyond that a long, low palace of light, and the light was blue-white, and almost solid; the deep darkness showed through just enough to make me see the building wasn't solid. And the architectonic light appeared to float off the ground, if there was ground.

He said, "La Place de la Concorde."

I thought, la Place de la Concorde.

We stopped in a wide, brightly lit street, under plane trees which cast the shadows of leaves on the taxi. I took up my bag and followed the man from the band to a large door with a brass handle in the middle; he unlocked it, and we went along a passageway into a courtyard, where windows shone yellow, and through a half-glass door at the far side of the courtyard. He pressed a button for illumination, and we went up a flight of carpeted stairs which creaked; the walls were hung with paintings in thick frames. On the third landing, he unlocked a door with a brass handle in its middle, and as he opened I saw, standing inside, a short, elderly woman, her grey hair held up about her head with combs and left curly on top. She had no doubt been coming towards the door when she heard the key; when she saw me come in with my bag after the man, she drew back, raised her head and pursed her lips. While the man spoke to her in what I recognized as Spanish, I glanced about the apartment, at its polished parquet floors, yellow-brown walls with dark paintings, and many spindly tables covered with embroidered cloths and porcelain bowls and figurines. I thought how odd it was that I would, in France, be staying among Spaniards. She turned to the man, her hand to her raised chin, and spoke in Spanish, and then she turned to me and spoke in clear, fine French.

The man from the ship introduced me to Madame Alberti.

I bowed a little.

"I don't mind having Americans stay," she said. "They are very polite."

She smiled, a clear, fine smile. "Come," she said, "I'll show you your room."

Worried that my suitcase would bang into a piece of furniture and knock over the figurines on it, I followed her carefully down a passage into a high, narrow room. She switched on the light and let me enter first. Against one wall was a wardrobe almost as big as the room, one of its doors open. She came in, moving with quick, little jerks, and shut the wardrobe door, then stood before me, her chin raised. I put my suitcase down.

"Thank you very much," I said in French.

"You'll take it."

I repeated, "Thank you very much."

"El señor is a friend of my daughter," she said, as if his

presence in her apartment needed an explanation. "I think he is leaving for Spain tomorrow." I wondered if she was pleased that he was leaving for Spain.

"Come, now, into my sitting room," she said, "and we can talk for some minutes."

In the sitting room, the man from the ship rose when Madame Alberti entered. We all stood by a round, cloth-covered table, from which Madame Alberti took a glass dish of shelled nuts. She held it out to me, and I took one, thanking her. "Take another," she said. I did, and held it in one hand while I ate the first with the other hand. She smiled at me and said, "Monsieur, vous êtes comme un écureuil." I asked her what an écureuil was. She explained, even acted it out, and the man suddenly said, "C'est un squirrel," and I wondered how he knew that word. Madame asked, "Quoi?" We all laughed.

Madame looked at me. She asked, "Monsieur l'Écureuil, when were you born?"

"In 1940," I answered.

She raised her hands. "A whole generation born during the war, but who can't possibly remember it."

I looked away from her.

The man asked me, "Are you hungry?"

"Oh," I said, "not very—"

"You must have something to eat," Madame said.

"I'll take you," the man said.

He took me to a café across the street, where we stood at a long zinc bar.

Though I was tired and hot and wanted to wash, I kept thinking: here I am, here I am.

He asked me what I'd like to drink, but I didn't know

what to ask for. I pursed my lips and shrugged as I'd seen him do, then said, "Du vin." He introduced me to a man and a woman behind the zinc; he spoke to them and I didn't understand, and I wondered what he was saying. They all pursed their lips and shrugged often. I drank my glass of wine and said, "Je suis extrêmement fatigué." He told me I should go to my room. He didn't mention food, and I knew he had asked me out to be polite. I said, yes, I would like to go to my room.

He let me into the apartment, where one pale yellow light was lit. The parquet creaked as we went silently to my door, outside of which he shook my hand and whispered, "Bonne nuit." I locked the door.

The bulb, which hung from a long cord in a fluted glass shade, threw fine needles of light, and between the needle-like beams was darkness. There was a bed with a lace counterpane and there were lace curtains over the window, which was shut. Hot, I went to the window, opened it wide, then, leaning out, pushed to open the shutters, and as I did I had an image of myself performing an authentic European act. I was, I told myself, in a room in Paris, and every act I performed there, however alone I was, was my first in Paris, and was made significant by Paris. My self-consciousness was justified by the whole of Paris, and when, opening the old shutters out, I saw, beyond trees and dark, square buildings, the illuminated top of the Eiffel Tower, and from its tip a great beam of light rising out at an angle into the wide summer sky, I stood at the window with the sense of being wholly justified.

The window open to cool air, I turned back into the room. I studied the details, and every detail, it seemed to me, was significant for being a detail of this first experience—each stain on the flowered wallpaper, tear in the lace curtains, threadbare patch in the carpet.

I was very frightened, and unpacked quietly, as though to let no one know I was there.

I thought: here, you are going to be different.

I needed a bath. I opened the door of my room a little to peer out into the now dark passage. I was unable to find a light switch. In the light from my room I went further along the passage to the bathroom. But when I turned the bath spigots on, no water came out. Back in my room, I shut the shutters and undressed, and tried to wash at the basin; but the water was cold, there was no soap, and the one towel was thin and narrow. My pajamas stuck to me with sweat. On the bed were many thick blankets, which I took off; the sheet was rough. I lay on my back in the middle of the hard, sagging bed, my chin on my chest because of the bolster under my head. I did not think: how uncomfortable this is. I thought: this is how Europeans sleep. I didn't sleep.

In the gray, grainy, early morning light, I woke to the incomprehensible shouts of children out in the courtyard.

I said a prayer in French to my private God to protect me.

I didn't feel well, not only because I hadn't eaten and hadn't slept; I felt as if I had a stone in my stomach which gave me cramps. But what I would see and hear, smell and taste and touch of the outside would save me from what I felt inside.

I told myself not to rely on God.

Shaving in cold water, I cut myself. I touched the blood on my jaw, then examined the drop on my finger. Instead of rinsing it off in the tap water, I looked about the room for what was its most secret spot—a spot, I decided, behind the headboard, just far enough from the wall so I could reach behind it—and there, on the back of the bed, I pressed the drop of blood.

I wondered if I should make my bed or not. I did, and straightened the room, I thought that anyone might, at any moment, come into the room, so I locked the door. I sat on the bed for a while, quiet. Then I went out.

I thought there was no one in the apartment, and was a little shocked when I heard, from a room as I passed, Madame Alberti call, "Monsieur." She was in the dining room, and asked me to come in. A newspaper was spread out on the table. She asked me to sit. In the center of the round table was a large porcelain bowl with porcelain leaves, flowers, and birds about the edge. She gave me a ballpoint pen and a yellow form which she said I must fill out for the police. Intentionally, I filled it out so it was hardly legible; I thought the police had no right to know where I was, even the French police. But Madame read it, pursed her lips, and said, "No, no, this won't do. I can't read it. You'll have to do it again." "I'm sorry," I said, and printed out carefully a new form, which she examined.

She gave me a set of keys, one for the street door when it was shut, told me she had spoken to the concierge about me, and told me to be quiet when I came in late.

She said, "Now, in the apartment, where there is porcelain, you put nothing. Do you understand? Nothing."

I said I understood.

The room was five hundred thirty francs a day.

"And now you'll have a cup of coffee with me," she said.

The coffee did nothing to help my stomach.

35

Madame Alberti asked me, "What will you see in Paris?"
"What should I see?" I asked.

She said, "See?" For a moment, she put the tips of her
fingers to her brow, so her eyes were covered, then she
lowered her hands. Her face was a little twisted. "What,
from your age and distance, you haven't seen! When it
came to me, yesterday evening, that you had not seen anything of the war, I was taken aback, you know. I hadn't
been made quite so aware of a new generation."

I asked, "Were you in Paris during the war?"

She waved a hand to indicate she would not talk about it.
She said, "There is so much to see in Paris. So much."

I went out with a map, which I kept hidden in my jacket
pocket. The morning was becoming hot and heavy. Floating
drops of moisture glared.

Out in the Parisian streets, I walked among Parisians.
When I got lost, I didn't take my map out to look at it, because I didn't want anyone to think I did not know where
I was, I did not want anyone to think I was not Parisian. I
was wearing my American striped jacket and vest, and I
was sweating.

Though I knew that in France I must, at all times, carry
identification—my passport—with me, I decided to carry
none. In America, I wasn't obliged to carry identification.

By the time I reached the Eiffel Tower, there was a heavy
mist. I was feeling very unwell, and thought I must try
to use a toilet. I found a public toilet among bushes, off
a gravel path; I was puzzled that in the men's toilet was a
woman, large and old, who held open for me the door to
a cubicle. It was a porcelain draining board with a hole.
I was constipated; trying to shit made me feel worse. When

I came out, I realized the woman attendant wanted money. I thought: in France you have to pay to shit? I came out of the public toilet into the heavy wet air.

The Eiffel Tower soared, in rising arcs, above me, and disappeared into the haze. I was weak, and sat on a little green metal chair on a gravel patch to look up into the tower. A man in a dirty, blue cotton jacket and a dirty, blue money pouch hanging from his waist came over to me and asked me for money. I paid him, got a ticket, and thought: in France, you have to pay to sit down? All activities in France had to be paid for.

I stared up into the tower, stared with the expectation that something would happen to me. I imagined that I would, somehow, be taken up into the tower, would be transformed into it, and would myself rise in arc upon arc above Paris.

But I would perhaps have to pay for that.

Though this was the moment for me to make a conscious claim to be of the world from which the Eiffel Tower soared, high into abstraction (to soar into abstraction was, I thought, French, and I was French, I understood the monument soaring in my blood, high over anything that had to do with daily living), I forced my thinking; I kept thinking, instead, of having to pay to shit and sit down.

My jacket over my arm, my vest and tie undone, my shirt wet with sweat, and my body smelling in the heat, I walked back to the apartment. No one was there, or if there was anyone, he or she was behind closed doors. I tried to sleep, but it was hotter in the room than outside. I couldn't control my thinking, couldn't, as I thought I must, sort out my consciousness; my thinking, my consciousness, were active in themselves, as though they had nothing to do with where I was. I half slept, and I saw images in flashes, heard distant sounds, which had nothing to do with Paris.

I half slept the day through, and in the evening felt a little better. I thought I must have something to eat. There was still no one in the apartment. The door to the Spaniard's room was open; the mattress was stripped, and I saw no personal effects. I went to the café, which served food, and, at a round, marble topped table, I ate a steak and pommes frites, which was all that I could understand from the purple stenciled menu; and I drank a bottle of wine. Drunk, I felt even better. The patron came to me to speak for a while; the patronne stood behind the zinc to speak to me. We talked about America. They did not seem to be very interested, but they were attentive. Then I realized I didn't know how to ask for the bill. I lingered at the table, embarrassed, as the patron and patronne served the customers; I finally said, in a loud voice, "Je suis fini," and everyone turned to me, amazed, and then they laughed. Still drunk, I walked up and down the boulevard. The cafés were crowded; I went to my room.

In bed, I took from my wallet a black and white photograph of my mother and father, and studied it.

The next day I went out into Paris with the sense of going out into the whole of the city, all at once. The city existed for me, not in its streets and squares and buildings, but as an idea, and in the same way a person might have an idea I imagined having Paris. I went out with my little camera. There was so much Paris, too much. I knew quickly I could not have it as an idea. It was soot black and brown, and water-streaked. I took many photographs, all from artistic angles. If I could not have Paris as a whole, all at once,

I would have it in its parts, however long it took me. I re-solved to take a photograph of everything I saw which im-pressed me. I took photographs of doorways, shop windows, bicycles leaning against old walls with torn posters. Through the bars of an iron railing, I photographed a clochard, an old beggar woman, lying on the pavement, and as I framed the picture, I thought: she has suffered. I needed to possess the whole of Paris, needed, somehow, to include it in a huge encyclopedia that would have in it every table and chair, every bottle and glass in Paris. As I walked about, I photographed the water running in the cobbled gutters, the rows of plane trees with mottled trunks, the pissoirs. I noted the shiny studs marking the pedestrian crossings, the circular gratings about trees.

I found the Seine, which I photographed from bridges, As I walked along a quai, other people walked along with me, couples with their arms about each other's waists. I saw a young man walking along with a girl, his hand inside her bodice and holding a breast.

I went to my room in the middle of the afternoon to un-dress and lie on my bed. When I opened my eyes to look, light through the curtains cast the shadows of lace flowers and leaves on my body. I dressed quickly to hide my body.

During that day, I went to my room three times before I finally went back for the night.

In the following days, I did not see Madame Alberti. It was as if she, too, had gone away, and I wondered where to. The concierge, a fat man, saluted me.

Before getting into my pajamas at night, I shut my shut-ters and bolted my door, and washed my body in cold water at the little wash basin. It was as if I, in the dim room, was exposing a secret which I did not want to expose. I quickly got into my pajamas. Then I opened my shutters and leaned out to look at the Eiffel Tower.

I never felt clean. I needed to wash in a gushing shower. Though I wore, now, chino trousers and a short-sleeved shirt in the heat, I still sweated, and I walked about in the smelly awareness of my body. One morning, as I was walking along the Seine, I noticed a poster advertising an open air pool on the river, and I decided I must go there, where there would be showers. In my wide, loose, boxer bathing suit, I sat, my arms and legs crossed, on a cement bench, and I watched the young Frenchmen and girls of my age play at the side of the pool; they wore tight bathing suits which clung to them and revealed their bodies, and, in a circle, they threw a red ball to one another. They didn't jump or shout, and only smiled at one another as they threw the ball. It seemed to me each one, boy or girl, was alone, and only in delicate contact with one another; and they appeared subtly sad. Sometimes they went to one another and touched one another, on the bare arm, shoulder, hip. They were sad, but they were not shy. I wondered if they remembered any of the war. Then one of them threw the ball into the pool, and they all dived in. I could see their bodies flash in the water. Go on, I told myself, go on. I remained on the concrete bench. I couldn't join them. I was frightened that I might accidentally touch, or be touched, by one. I left the pool without having a shower.

At a café in the Latin Quarter, I sat with my demi. At a table next to mine, three young men were leaning towards one another and talking. They wore, despite the heat, dark, tight-fitting suits and thin-soled, pointed shoes, and they appeared cool. They spoke rapidly, and they had serious expressions.

40

My bathing suit rolled up in my hand, I walked up the Boulevard St. Michel. I stayed in the shade of the plane trees. Under the awnings of shops were large tables piled with clothes, and from time to time I stopped to look at these. Then I bought a cheap pair of black trousers, tight about the ankles, a white shirt with a flared collar, and narrow, very pointed black shoes, and I went back to my room to change quickly into them. Dressed in these, I went to the Luxembourg Garden. I stayed where there were few people and the shrubbery was scruffy, but, with a sense of daring that was also an act of will, I walked out into the Latin Quarter, among the young Parisians. I sweated, not entirely from the heat.

I stayed out all day. My feet burned. I stopped at many cafés.

It was partly because I was tired from walking—and I was now walking through Paris, linking one part to another—and partly for reasons which had to do with literature, that I stopped at the cafés. I sat outside, on wooden platforms, under awnings, and wrote a letter to my parents, then a longer one to my brother Albert. And when I stopped writing, I thought about Hemingway.

There was deceit in Hemingway, I realized, because he had made me believe that he could take Europe entirely for granted, could take easy possession of it, whereas I saw now that he couldn't have. In Paris, I recognized this in Hemingway (or imagined it in Hemingway and recognized it in myself): that he was as self-conscious as any American, but, in America, there had been no object far enough outside the self-consciousness, or, perhaps, foreign enough to his self-consciousness, to stand in its own right; here, in Paris, the object—the beaded glass of beer on the round

41

green metal table—stood on its own, stood outside you, was really foreign, and it was, because of that, an object of joy. (I thought, "Because of that," but I couldn't say why.) Not that Hemingway, or I, saw the European objects as Europeans saw them; we didn't—we couldn't—because we were Americans. We saw the objects as Americans abroad would; and we saw them, not as objects of an inner world, but objects of an outer world radiating in all directions, beyond our self-consciousness. I walked through the Latin Quarter, staring at every stone. I stopped at a fruit barrow by the side of a cobbled street, where a thin woman in black was throwing handfuls of cherries into a tin scale hanging off the back of the barrow; the cherries bounced against the tin in the bright light, and I looked with amazement at the cherries.

I felt far from America.

My first Sunday in Paris, I thought, well, if I must fulfill the obligation I had to go to church, I'll go to Notre Dame. The cathedral was black inside. I found a service being held in a side chapel, and stood outside, among others both standing and kneeling or sitting on the low, high backed chairs; there was some movement, even talk, among the congregation. I allowed myself to be distracted by the black pillars and vaulting. Then the priest, in his chasuble, came to the top of the stone steps which led down from the chapel to give a sermon, and I found myself in the French parish church in America. I had heard that voice from Monsieur le Curé—flat, addressing no one in particular and everyone in general, and flatly absolute—and I realized I had not come far. The Mass was, in every detail, familiar to me. Some of the old women who went to Communion, the sleeves of their dresses tight about their fat arms, could have been going to Communion at the parish church. I felt obliged to pay attention, but it was an obligation I resented; I hadn't come to Paris to stand, against my will, at a Mass.

I stood till the end, then, feeling hollow, went out to the park at the back of the cathedral, along the wall over the Seine, and down to the quai. Thick banks of ivy hung down the stone walls to the quai side. I walked along in sunlight that was, for the first time, not hot and wet, but light, léger, and other people were walking with me, couples with arms about one anothers' waists. The Mass I had been to seemed to have had only to do with me, not with them; if I was French, I was an older kind of Frenchman, much older than these strollers, these flâneurs, because my religion was the religion of their ancestors. I did not want to be a dark ancestor.

I slept through the hot Sunday afternoon, and woke feeling unwell. For the first time, I thought: I hate France. I went out. The night was as warm as the day. I was sitting at a café drinking a beer, which I had ordered in brief French, imagining the waiter, if I did not say much, would take me, in my French clothes, for French. An old woman without teeth came to me with a little basket over one arm and held out to me a nosegay of violets. I said, "Non, merci," and smiled. She reached out and touched my cheek with a knuckle and said, "Comme il est mignon." I drew back, and she, no doubt imagining she had offended me, turned away. I touched my cheek, thinking: she took me for French.

I went to my room. I had been in it over a week, and I had not seen Madame since the first morning. Again, I tried to wash myself, then washed some socks and underpants. I did not know what I would do when it came, soon, to having shirts and pajamas washed. In my pajamas, I opened the shutters and sat at the rickety table by an open window to write in my diary what I had seen, heard, touched, tasted, smelled during the past day, but after a while I had to give it up, there was too much.

I went the next morning to sit on the edge of a quai, under a stone wall covered with ivy, and watch the couples.

As I was coming into the apartment later that day, Madame Alberti was leaving. She did not seem at all surprised that we hadn't seen one another. When she said something about the bill, I thought, of course, in Paris that's what's most important. I said I would pay her right away, and she said, no, that wasn't necessary, then, after considering a moment, she said, yes, that was agreeable, and it would be most agreeable if I could pay in American dollars. I gave her some dollars, which she put into her purse before going out, thanking me. I thought: the daily world of American dollars.

Before I went to my room, I asked her, timidly, when I might have baths. She told me, "Every day if you wish," and told me a bath would cost extra. I said, "I thought that." Then she asked me if I had clothes to be washed, and suggested a blanchisserie.

I sat on my bed and stared at the armoire, then I went out again. It was a bright, clear afternoon. I found myself walking down the Boulevard St. Michel, the fresh air eddying. I was walking behind a couple, a young man and woman, who sauntered slowly. It was as if they had just got out of bed together, and half asleep, were fumbling a little at one another. Their clothes were soft and wrinkled. They turned at a corner, and I followed them to an entrance in a long, black, blank wall, the entrance, I saw, to the Cluny museum, and I went in after them, across a courtyard and through a door which the young man held open for me. I stood close behind them as I waited to buy a ticket. The young man had one hand under his girlfriend's collar, grasping, under the cloth, her naked shoulder.

I looked at objects in glass cases with them. Sometimes I turned away from them and caught them in reflection in the glass of another case. I tried to concentrate on the delicate objects: a tooled leather box, buckles, thin chains and clasps. I fixed on a medieval leather shoe, and when I looked up the couple was gone. I went into the next room, a room of tapestries, but the couple was not there.

I had lost them. I wanted to sit but could not find a seat. I walked from room to room, then down a flight of stone steps, and, down more steps, I entered a large, high, vaulted room, with walls of small, rough stones tightly fitted together, where there was no one. Hesitant, I looked about the room, unsure, because of its emptiness, if anyone was allowed in. I walked gently through the great hall, towards an arched doorway, and down worn steps to a lower level, narrow, where there was an iron railing separating me from a deep level, so deep I could have killed myself if I had fallen over into it. Above, hanging from the high vaults, were great black cobwebs. I leaned over and saw, at the bottom, some broken sarcophagi, one with crosses carved on the lid. And to the right of this deeper level was a doorway with steps leading down to an even deeper level, but I could not see beyond the first few steps, which led into darkness.

4

I FELT totally seul.

From the museum, I went to try to find Chris and Harry, my friends from college, at their hotel, the name and address of which they had given me. It was in an area I did not know. I stopped a man in a trim uniform, and he saluted me. I asked him for directions and he, with an elaborate politeness, indicated them to me. I tried to be as polite back. As I was leaving him, it occurred to me he was not a policeman, but a military officer.

I knocked on Chris and Harry's door, at the end of a corridor, and Chris opened. He was surprised to see me, as if, in a strange city, he could not believe he'd meet anyone he knew.

He said, "I wondered what happened to you."

"I've been trying to make myself at home in Paris," I said.

I felt empty, as if I had no lungs, heart, liver, bowels.

Half leaning out of the door, he said, "Oh, I don't like Paris. I know you're French, and I'm sorry, but I don't like the French."

I laughed. "The French think I'm American," I said.

"I want to go back to America," he said.

He opened the door wider and I followed him into his room. Harry was lying on one of the two beds. It appeared that they never left the room. Chris lay on the other bed. They both lit cigarettes.

I said, "Well, tell me what you've seen."

"Nothing," Chris said.

"He doesn't want to leave the room," Harry said.

"Where do you eat?" I asked.

"In self services," Chris said. "We haven't had a real meal in two weeks."

"He doesn't want to go anywhere where he has to speak French," Harry said.

"As if you did," Chris turned on him. "You can't say shit in French."

I said, "Look, I'll take you to a restaurant."

I told myself I didn't want to be with them. I wanted to be among Frenchmen. I found, directing them through the Left Bank streets, that I was demonstrating to them my familiarity, my native familiarity, with Paris. To them, I might always have known Paris.

In the traiteur, at a white cloth covered table, I translated the menu for Chris and Harry. They were glum, but when the roast pork and mashed potatoes arrived their faces changed; they had perhaps thought that abroad they would not be able to get food they recognized. Chris asked for mayonnaise on his salad, and I asked the waitress, who frowned. I said, shrugging, "They put mayonnaise on their salad," and she, shrugging more, went to ask the cook to make up a little glass bowl of mayonnaise, which she brought to the table, smiling. I ordered a French meal, which Chris and Harry looked upon as from a great distance: cold brains for first, then kidneys in a wine sauce, and a cooked salad. I wanted them to see I could eat, because I was French, what they never could.

At the next table a man was reading a newspaper. He lowered it when the waitress came and placed a white plate before him on which I saw boudin, the black sausage I had thought no one but the people of my parish in America ate. I stared at it, stared as the man stuck his fork into it and broke the skin with his knife. Boudin.

After lunch, I walked with my college friends around the quarter. If I had some remote claim to be here, to belong to France, I wanted to choose those claims, and they did not include boudin. I wanted to claim my own Paris, which had to be stranger than anything I'd known before I came. If my parents had been Parisians, I thought, they would have eaten boudin in their local traiteur. There was an everyday world in Paris which was as everyday as the parish.

"Let's go down by the Seine and watch the lovers," I said.

We walked down to the Seine, and paused now and then to look at the contents of the bouquinists, the old books, photographs, warped vellum pages from old hymnals, and I reached for a book which had an English title, a paperback book with green covers, and as I opened it I saw, in solid print, the word "fuck." I had never before seen that word printed. Other words jumped out and struck me, in the forehead, in the stomach, in the groin: "cock," "cunt." I didn't show it to the others, but put it back and walked off, in a state similar to that of a boy who has just had his first orgasm without quite knowing what it was.

I wanted to go to my little room. But I remained with

my college friends. Back in their hotel room, we drank wine, and talked about ourselves, and then we talked about sex.

Chris said, "I came to Europe hoping that I'd lose my virginity. I hate my virginity. I don't want it. But no one here wants it either."

We laughed.

Harry smoked. "Maybe you should go with a prostitute."

"Maybe," Chris said. "Maybe."

"I could show you the places to go to," I said.

Chris said, "But I wouldn't know what to say."

"Say? You wouldn't have to *say* anything," Harry said.

Drunk, we laughed more.

I didn't reveal anything about myself.

There was a knock on their door, and Chris opened. In came friends they'd made at the hotel, three young English women and one Englishman. We all took swigs from a big bottle of wine, and when that was empty another bottle was uncorked by the Englishman.

Chris kept calling out, "Let's give in, let's give in and lose control—"

I said, "I'm going to undress."

"Come on," Chris said. "Undress. Let it happen."

I unbuttoned my shirt.

One of the English girls said, "You can't do that."

"What do you mean I can't do it?" I said. "Where are we, in America, that I can't do what I want?"

I stood, and I went cold as I pulled my shirttails out of my trousers. I was going to give my body to the world as I wanted it to be given, and was not going to have it taken away from me. I unbuttoned the cuffs and pulled the shirt off and threw it down. I yanked off my shoes, and,

49

swiftly, all in one continuous motion, undid my belt, unzipped my trousers, and, placing my thumbs under the elastic band of my underpants, pushed down and removed them and my trousers together, stepping out of them as I leaned against a wall. My socks still on, I remained leaning against the wall, and I looked at the people in the room, who were all laughing, even the English. Harry was hunched over, his hands to his stomach, laughing. I was cold and felt my skin pucker in patches. I made myself smile.

Suddenly, I ran into the bathroom and vomited into the toilet, then lay on the white and black tile floor and passed out.

When I woke in the morning I was in the bathtub, a blanket tucked about me. Lined up along the side of the bath was a long row of empty bottles, and there was a smell of wine gone sour. But I felt well, felt, even, bright, and I got out of the tub and, the blanket around me, watched the tub fill with hot water. I got back in and lay for a long time in the water. In the bedroom, Chris and Harry, sprawled on the one bed, were asleep. I dressed quietly, taking my clothes from a chair.

The morning was clear, and before I returned to my room I walked through the Luxembourg Gardens to look at the naked statues among the clipped hedges.

5

AGAIN in the empty apartment, I wandered, from time to time delicately touching a porcelain figure or bowl. I picked one up and was examining it when Madame Alberti came into the room. The apartment had not been empty. She said nothing.

I said, "This is pretty," and put it down.

She studied me for a while, and I expected her to say something that was a conclusion of her studying me, but she asked me if I would like to have a cup of tea with her.

"Thank you," I said, "that would be a pleasure."

"You've been too much alone."

At tea, she asked me what I had seen of Paris. I thought out my sentences carefully as I told her. She said, "But you've seen nothing yet. Nothing." I asked, "What places should I see?" She smiled.

As I helped her to bring the tea things into the kitchen, we continued to talk. The doorbell rang, and she went to answer. As though I were doing something I knew I shouldn't, I waited in the passage. I saw Madame, moving quickly, show two men into her sitting room, on which she closed the door. A moment later the doorbell rang again, and Madame hurried to answer. In came a large woman, and she, too, was taken into the sitting room, and the door was closed.

Madame was in her dim sitting room, the door open, when I came in from supper. Quickly, she got up and lit another lamp and invited me in. She asked me where I'd eaten, and approved and disapproved of the restaurant, asked me what I'd eaten, and approved and disapproved of the food, and asked me what I'd paid, which was both reasonable and unreasonable. She seemed to want me to stay with her, and I wanted to stay with her, but we were silent. She shook my hand good night. She looked very tired, but I had an idea she wouldn't be able to sleep. She went into her room.

In the morning, on the way to the bathroom for a bath, I saw, in the passage outside the sitting room, Madame talking quietly with the large woman. The woman turned away from me abruptly, as if she did not want me to see her face.

As I was going out, Madame met me. She said, "Monsieur l'Écureuil, you mustn't wear your belt down around your hips, but around your waist. Why do Americans wear their belts so low?"

I tightened my belt as she watched me.

She said, "Don't be offended by my daughter. She dislikes Americans."

"Why?" I asked.

"You ask?"

I saw in Madame's eyes the question: how can you, an American, not know about your country?

Coming back in, I heard voices from Madame's sitting room. As I hurried past I glanced inside: my eyes met

Madame Alberti's, but she remained straight in a chair and made no sign that she'd seen me. Before her on a settee were her daughter and one of the men. I went to my room.

After I heard the daughter and the man leave, I heard Madame walk up and down the passageway, often passing my door. I was lying on my bed. She knocked. A little fear went through me, as though she would come into the room and find me doing something I shouldn't have been doing. I jumped up and opened the door.

She said she was sorry she had disturbed me, and she looked at me with the wonder of why she had.

She smiled. "You are the first to know. My daughter is to marry."

"I'm very happy to know that."

"Come to my sitting room."

I followed her in.

She said, "He's a Communist." She shrugged. "No doubt she's right. She'll join the Party before they marry."

There could not have been, to me, anyone more different than a Communist. Madame's daughter became strange. I wanted to meet her. I thought she would like me.

Madame, walking about the room, appeared a little frightened. She said to me, frowning, "You see, her father was a Communist in Spain. He was killed in the civil war there."

I could only nod.

She stopped, and frowned more. "Do you know what that means?" she said. Bringing her hands together as in prayer, she touched her chin, and she said, "No, you don't know."

She sat on the settee, and I thought I should leave her.

While, two days later, I, at the dining room table, was reading a novel I'd bought cheaply from a bouquiniste along the Seine, Madame came in from outside with her daughter. Talking Spanish to one another, they entered the dining room, and I stood.

The daughter came to the table, picked up the novel and said to her mother in French, "You allow such a writer's books in the house?"

Madame said, "But he can, from time to time, write well."

Her daughter made a face. "I can only hope Americans read fascist collaborators' books in the same way they leave lights on in rooms they aren't in—it means nothing to them."

"Americans are very polite," Madame said.

"They drink water from the tap in the kitchen and they don't peel their fruit before eating it. They walk barefoot from the bathroom, through the apartment, to their rooms. They don't wash out the bath after they use it."

All of this she knew I did or didn't do. Her mother must have told her. I hunched my shoulders.

She said, "Americans—"

But I didn't want to hear her talk about Americans. To her, everything about me was all outside me, all in my being American. I had no inside.

Madame's daughter said, "They have as little knowledge of politics as they have of manners."

I looked up at Madame's daughter, at her big, dark face, and it came to me that I had, all the while I was abroad, never stopped thinking that I was American. It was like being black, and being made to think all the time of being black.

Embarrassed by her daughter, Madame said to me, "We know so little about America. Where do you live there?"

I was going to make the daughter look me in the eyes. She was looking beyond me.

I could say that I was, really, French, that, by blood, I was French, as they weren't. But that wouldn't have meant anything to them.

I said, "Oh, in America, I live among Red Indians. My great grandmother was a Blackfoot. My aunts and uncles smoke pipes made from ears of corn, and they smear their bodies with bear grease in the winter to keep warm."

I didn't smile when the daughter glanced at me.

The doorbell rang. The daughter went quickly and came back into the dining room with six or seven people, men and women, whom I was not introduced to. I picked up my books and left as they formed a circle about the dining room table, and I heard them, from my room, talking in Spanish. Passing quietly to go out, I saw them, the daughter and her fiancé among them, about the lace covered table, having tea from fine white cups, and behind them the French windows stretched over with white muslin through which the light was finely diffused.

Madame was not with them.

They were still there when I came in. In my room, I wrote in my diary how seul I was. I heard Madame's voice among the others, as, I imagined, the visitors left. Then there was silence. I wondered if I should go out and help Madame clear up, but I remained in my room, writing. I heard her clear, and then I heard her walk up and down the passage. She knocked on my door, finally, and asked me if I would like to have a light supper with her.

In the evening, hot, we went for a long walk. We walked along the Seine to the Pont Neuf, and from the bridge went down the stone steps to the point of the Île de la Cité.

55

Under the arches of the bridge a group of Algerian young men were playing drums, flutes, and dancing about; the light from the globed lamps made their skin gleam. Madame and I watched them, among others who had also stopped to watch them. Then there was, piercing through the music, a whistle, and before any of the spectators could move the Algerians were gone; all about us were the police asking the spectators for identification, and I had none. When a flic came up to Madame, she presented her identity card. When he looked at me, I said, in English, "I don't understand." I wanted him to know I was an American. He said, in English, "Passport." I said nothing. Then Madame calmly, as if this were something she had had to do often, spoke in rapid French, and the policeman took out a thin blue folder and tapped it against his palm and said to me in French, "Even I have to carry identification, everyone has to," and he left. Madame said to me, "You must carry your passport with you." "Yes," I said, but I thought: no, I won't.

As we walked back to the apartment, I asked, "What was that about?"

"But you must know," Madame said. "You must."

"Oh yes."

"You're not aware of what's going on in the world."

"I know."

We stopped just inside the courtyard.

She said, "Tell me what you know about the war here in Europe."

I said, "I know there was great suffering."

She left me to speak to the concierge about something, she said.

After the incident under the Pont Neuf, I noticed there

were many policemen in Paris standing beside high, gun-metal barriers, carrying machine guns.

Out for the day, wandering, I came back to the apartment to find Madame having tea at the dining room table with the man from the boat. He had been to Spain. He asked me how I was getting on, and I, lowering my head, said, "Bien."

Madame smiled at me, a clear, intelligent smile. "What have you been doing?"

I told her I'd spent the afternoon at the Louvre.

Still smiling, she studied me. She said, "I have already said, you are too much on your own."

I raised my chin.

"Listen to me," she said. "What one thinks and feels about oneself is never very important."

"No," I said.

With a soft sigh, she said, "We'll have dinner here this evening, you and I."

I left them to go to my room and try to sleep.

At dinner with Madame, I felt I wanted to confide in her something, but I had no idea what; she, maybe sensing that, asked me questions about my parents, thinking I missed them. I realized she would never ask me the questions I wanted her to ask: questions about the state of my feelings and thinking. Her discreet questions had to do with my outside being; about my inside being there was nothing to ask, because there was nothing there. And she was right: my thoughts and feelings were nothing. As we talked, I found I was becoming better; I was surprised that she was, as if it had been her intention, taking me out of my inner self, which was nowhere, and engaging me in the outer self, which was a world to be discovered beyond anything I knew. She served thin veal steaks, cheese, fruit, and a carafe of wine.

Apart from her, I knew no one in Paris except for Chris and Harry, and I didn't want to see them. I hadn't seen them since the night I got drunk, and I knew they didn't know how to get in touch with me. After three days of wandering, looking, I went to their hotel. In their room, they said little to me, slowly smoking cigarettes, as if I had betrayed them. They wanted to leave Paris. They hated Paris more than ever. The city was hot and land-locked and they wanted to feel free.

In a café, we had a discussion about nudity. Chris said he was amazed by all the painted and sculptured nude bodies he'd seen in Europe. When I said, "Why are you amazed? Don't you know what bodies look like?" he frowned at me. I said, "What do Americans think is wrong with the naked body?" Harry said, "We don't think there's anything wrong. My parents have a little marble Venus, but they keep it in a drawer in my father's wardrobe in their bedroom. They'd never put it out." "That's strange," I said.

I did not want to be with Chris and Harry. Everything they said and did was familiar to me, and as much as I wanted to be unlike them, I wasn't; and they would see I wasn't. They were as I should have been.

Madame was not in. It was imperative that I should talk to her; I felt there was something important she had to tell me, something I wanted her to tell me. At her round dining room table, I took a chair. The table shone in the late sunlight through the French windows. At the center was a crocheted doily, and on the doily a cut crystal bowl of peaches, and I stared at the bowl and the fruit, edged in fine, variegated light.

Restless, I went out and walked to St. Germain, where I sat at a café. I looked at the people passing, and, beyond the people, the traffic, and beyond the traffic more people at a corner café on the other side of the street. I saw Angela Johnson at a table with two men, one white, one black; her hair was pulled back tightly and appeared polished, and she was talking and laughing with the men. I thought that she wouldn't want to see me or that I didn't want to see her, or perhaps both. And yet, as I sat still, my body urged me up to go to her, as if it were urging me to take a risk. I watched her get up with the men and walk off, slowly. She disappeared among the pedestrians, stopping now and then to touch one of the men and point.

The apartment was dim when I got back. In the dimness, Madame was sitting at her dining room table, her hands crossed and resting on the edge, her head lowered. Her eyes were unfocused, and the corners of her mouth turned down; with a creak of the parquet, she lifted her head, saw me, and she made her eyes focus and brighten as she made herself smile. She finally asked, "What is it?" I made myself smile, and I asked her if I could invite her to dinner at a small restaurant in the quarter that evening. She said she would like that.

At dinner, I asked her, as if it were the subject most distant from my vain self, about Europe during the war.

On the way home, in the light of street lamps, she pointed out to me, on black buildings, bullet-strafed walls.

6

ONE morning, as I was coming in from an hour at a café to study the paper, Madame called me from the dining room, where she, too, was reading a newspaper spread out on the table. For a while we discussed the news, I implying I knew more than I did by saying "Ah oui," to whatever she stated with authority. She must have known I was putting it on, but she indulged me; perhaps she thought that, after all, everyone put it on.

After a pause, she said, "Monsieur l'Écureuil, I'm sorry to tell you that I'll be going on holiday for three weeks, during which time I can't have anyone in the apartment, what with the porcelain and all—"

It occurred to me that I hadn't thought I'd have to leave this apartment.

Raising her chin and squaring her shoulders, she asked, "What do you know about Spain?"

I blushed and had to admit I knew nothing.

She talked about Spain. She talked about the coasts and the inland areas, the mountains and the plains. She mentioned the chestnut woods on the high hills, the green country and the rivers, the red dust. She described walking under the palms of an old city on a cliff above the sea, hot during the day but cool at night. And then she said, "I know you are a person who is drawn to strange places. Spain is a strange country."

"In what way?"

She laughed lightly. "If I told you, you would know and there would be no reason for you to go."

I raised a hand.

"Go to Spain," she said. She added quickly, "There is someone I'd like you to visit there, in the south."

I told myself I must do exactly as she said.

"Thank you," I said.

"Then you'll go?"

She got up, with quick movements, to go to the sideboard for paper, envelope, pen, as if they had been set there for a reason, and she came back to the table with them. Writing out a note, she pressed her forehead with a finger of her left hand. Having inserted the letter into the envelope, she sealed and addressed it.

But it was as if, handing it to me, she wanted to take it away. Hesitating, she said, "My daughter said you would like to see Spain."

"Your daughter?"

"She is not a bad person. I promise you she is a good person."

As I took the envelope, I knew I wasn't going to go to Spain.

"Merci bien," I said.

Paris was closed for holidays. Flies buzzed in the closed air.

At night, about to fall asleep, images of America flashed behind my closed eyes.

In bed, my last night in Madame Alberti's apartment, I was restless. I got up, dressed in clothes that were slightly damp from my sweat, and went out and walked up and down the Boulevard St. Germain. The cafés were lit and crowded; I passed them. In the dark, under a plane tree, on the pavement, was a small group of people, and as I went by I slowed down to see what was going on. A black man, with a beard, was crouched down by the building and laying out cards, face down, on the paving, and was saying, "Vas-y, vas-y," to another black man, crouched to the side of him, whose eyes shifted from the cards up to the spectators and back to the cards. I heard the dealer say, in American, "Come on," to the other black man, who, now concentrating on the cards, pointed to one with a long black finger, which the dealer picked up, turned over, and threw down. That these black men were American drew me in closer to watch them. The dealer said, "You've got it," and, still crouched, he took from his back pocket a folded thousand-franc note and gave it to the winner, who, his eyes wide, smiled up at the spectators. The dealer collected the cards, shuffled them, and said in a thick accent, "Qui veut jouer? Allez-y. Allez-y." No one of the five or six spectators moved, and then a man, who might have been German, said in English, "I will." "Then get yourself down here where you can see," the dealer said, and the player crouched. I watched the black hands deal out the cards. The German and the spectators were distracted by a young white woman with long hair and a toque who edged in along the wall beside the dealer, where she crouched, too. As everyone went back to concentrating on the cards, she extended an arm and touched the dealer's neck; he didn't move; and then she leaned towards him and said something, and he quickly picked up all the cards, stacked them, and put them into a pocket as he stood. He said, "C'est fini," and he, the girl, and the other black walked away. I turned in the opposite direction and saw two policemen coming towards us. I walked slowly, straight towards them, and I looked at them as I passed them in the street light shining through the plane trees.

Again, I did not have my passport on me.

Back in my room, I told myself that I wished I had played the card game.

I went out again. I sat at a café which was half empty. I tried to read a newspaper. I was not intelligent, I knew, and my lack of intelligence was evident to me whenever I tried to sort out, say, some crude understanding of politics from the newspapers.

I was looking at a carafe of water in the electric light on the empty table next to mine. From time to time, the water vibrated a little.

I left money under a saucer and walked away, down a side street off the boulevard.

If they made me feel joy, objects made me feel, too, that they were the visible points of some great, invisible suffering, as though they had survived a devastation, a great war, in which everything but these objects had been destroyed. Deeper than joy, I had a pity for them as if they were all that was left of life in a death camp—false teeth and hanks of hair and shoes and purses. They existed in a great darkness, the objects, and I searched in them for what made them objects of my American compassion and belief that they, by their survival, could help me survive. I loved these objects with an American love.

On the strength of the principle of one's duty, not to oneself, but to the society in which one lives, and is dependent upon, I should have become political, but I did not. I was a young man without the strength of will to fulfill any duty towards others which I might have felt imposed on me; I told myself I was an individual above all. I would only do what I wanted to do. From the point of view of the person I should have become, but didn't, I knew I was a decadent, a kind of criminal.

When I came out of a side street into the Boulevard St. Germain to the café where I'd been sitting, still brightly lit but almost deserted under its dark awning, I saw Angela. She appeared to be waiting for someone. As I approached, she squinted at me, then she smiled a large smile and raised both hands, standing a little from her chair. It was as if I were the person she was waiting for.

She hugged and kissed me, her thin body all angles; then she stepped back and looked at me and said: "You look different."

I was excited, and kept spilling the drink I ordered onto my chin, shirt, hands.

"Tell me what you've been up to," I said.

She laughed and put her hand over her mouth and hunched forward.

"Has it been bad?" I asked.

For an answer she just shook her hand as if to shake water off it; she was still laughing.

"Tell me," I said.

"I can't."

"Come on."

"No, no," she said.

"I thought you weren't staying in Paris."

"I'm on the verge of going."

"To Barcelona?" I asked.

"How did you know I was going to Barcelona?"

"You told me."

"Did I?"

"You told me you were going to see some American."

The skin of her face went taut. "I told you that?"

"You did."

She ran the tip of a long finger around her face, along her hair line, down by her ear, under her jaw, and up again to a temple. She dropped her hand. "Yes," she said, "I'm going to Barcelona to see some American."

"Hasn't he been waiting for you?"

She smiled.

I said, "I'm going to Spain, too."

"Aren't you supposed to start your studies?"

"Not for a month yet."

"Where will you go in Spain?"

"I have a letter to give to someone in the south."

I asked her if she would like another drink, and she said yes. I thought she would have said no.

Part Two

I

ON the train, I shared a compartment with four sleeping strangers slumped in their seats. The compartment was dark except for the little blue light on the ceiling, and the blind was drawn. The train rattled. My head shook against the wing of my seat. I kept half falling asleep, but the jostling woke me.

I did fall asleep, and woke up drooling. Wiping my saliva from the side of my face with my hand, I tried to see the dark shapes in the compartment.

I was going to Spain. Madame Alberti had let me know this: that I must never talk to anyone there about the Civil War. The country's dictator, Generalissimo Franco, had not won the war against the people, but pressed it into silent secrecy. I was going into a country at war with itself.

When, in the cold morning, I got down from the French train with my suitcase at the border to go through customs, I remarked, in the gray concrete building where the Spanish separated themselves from the non-Spanish into different lines, that there were many soldiers with rifles, wearing shiny black hats which stuck out at the back, and that they stood close to the line of Spaniards and watched them;

the non-Spanish line, in which I stood, moved quickly, and when I held out my American passport, green and stamped all over with the national seal, to a soldier on the other side of the barrier, he only glanced at it and waved me on. It seemed to me I was a long time on the Spanish train, with its narrow gauge wheels, before I saw, coming along the platform with bags and cardboard boxes and bundles, the first Spaniards to get through the military guards into their own country.

I fell asleep.

In the crowded Barcelona train station, I bumped into people with my big suitcase. I went to an information desk, and, instead of speaking English, asked in French about the next train to the town outside the city where Angela had told me to go. But I did not understand the woman, and, embarrassed, I had to ask again in English. The train was to leave in two hours. I bought my ticket and waited in the station buffet.

A boy came towards me along the tables with a shoe shining box slung over a shoulder by a strap; he put the box down before me and said something, and I, looking about to see if anyone was looking at me, said quietly, "Non, non," and waved a hand. But he squatted before me, shoved the box between my feet, and, because I didn't want anyone to think I was a foreigner, I slouched back on my chair and placed a shoe on top of the box. I did not look at the boy as he shined my shoes; I wondered how much money I should give him. The boy spoke to me and I simply raised my chin to him. In a loud voice which everyone could hear the boy said something more, and held up to me in a shoe-polish stained hand two rubber soles. I did not know what the boy was saying. I reached into my jacket for money, and handed what I thought was a big enough bill to the boy. But he sat cross legged on the ground before me and lifted my polished shoes each in turn into his lap, twisted my ankles, and nailed onto the bottoms of my shoes, with tiny tacks he appeared to take from between his teeth, the soles. There was nothing I could do but let him; I kept my eyes fixed on a glass of beer on a table. Standing before me now, the boy said something, and I made a face and once more held out the bill. The boy shook his head and said in a loud voice, "Hundred." I lifted my feet to look at the thick soles nailed under my soles, and I blushed. Again, I reached into my pocket and unfolded a hundred pesetas, and, without looking at him, handed it to the boy, who took it and left. Confused, I left too much money by my cup and rose onto my false soles and picked up my suitcase. Unbalanced by the soles, I walked through the station.

I said interrogatively to the only other traveller with me in the compartment, a woman in black, the name of the town I wanted to go to, and she nodded yes. Then she said, pointing to the window, "El mar," and I watched the sea, as the train passed along the coast, rise up and fall back in waves.

Before the train stopped at the station, I spotted Angela. She was standing on the small station platform, looking into the carriage windows, but she didn't see me.

She appeared blacker than I remembered.

I waited for a moment. The woman in the compartment leaned from her seat to touch my arm and repeat the name of the town. I took my valise and got out.

Angela stepped back as I approached her. In a short, loose, white dress, her black body showed through the sheer white.

"Hi," she said.

71

Passengers were going off in all directions into the late afternoon light.

"How did you know I'd be on this train?" I asked.

"What?" she said, frowning at me. Then she said, "Hey," and walked away from me, into an angle of bright light, and when she came out she had her arm in the arm of a plump, bald man whose clothes were twisted, and one shirttail out. She was skipping a little at his side, laughing and talking. They came to me, and Angela said to me, "How about that? I just caught sight of Hal here. The last time I saw him was the last time I was in Spain. How about that, seeing him now?"

It surprised me that I thought, as if I had been anticipating meeting him: but this can't be her man?

She introduced us. Hal, an American, held out his hand to me and said, "Put it there." His hand was soft.

He and Angela walked arm in arm out of the station and I, carrying my big valise, tried to keep up with them. We went through the crowded square outside the station. People's tanned bodies, in loose clothes, emanated rays. The cobbles and walls, too, emanated rays in all directions.

Angela and Hal sat at a café table on the cobbles and I sat with them, my valise at my side. Hal ordered glasses of rum. He didn't ask what I wanted, but, without saying anything to me, placed the glass before me.

They spoke in Spanish. They spoke for a long while, during which Hal ordered more rum. I drank a second glass as they talked.

Angela's short dress was so loose, it seemed with one small jerk of her body it would fall off. She untied and tied, again and again, the long thin cord about her waist, all that kept her dress wrapped close to her. She touched her body often. sometimes inserting her hand inside the top to hold a naked breast.

I thought: I don't know her at all.

She sat back, slumped, on her café chair, her long arms hanging loosely at her sides. My hands were on the table. Jolting me, she all at once reached a hand out and grabbed one of mine and yanked my arm so I turned to her.

"You'll see," she said.

With a third rum, I was drunk. Angela and Hal continued to talk in Spanish. Whenever Hal lifted his shoulders and chest and put out his arms, Angela, a little bit later, did the same. If he used a word in English or French, she, too, used it. In my drunken mind I began to speak and gesture as he did. I drank as he drank, not in sips but swallows.

We sat while the rays around us darkened.

"You'll see," Angela said to me, "We're going to do a lot that's terrific. I like doing things I've never done before. Don't you?"

"Yes."

"Have you ever climbed a mountain?"

"No."

"We'll climb a mountain."

As I was in her country, I had to accept Angela reducing me to someone who knew nothing.

Hal said to her, "I forgot to tell you—," and went on in Spanish, and she got excited by what he said, repeating, "No, no, no es posible," and laughing when he laughed.

I was very drunk.

Finally Hal looked at his watch and said, "I've got to go."

Angela said, "Listen."

"What?"

She winced a little, as though she thought he might hit her. "I'm out of money."

His plum face suddenly went thin. "You mean, you want me to pay for the drinks?"

"Well—"

"But I can't, cara. You knew I couldn't." He looked at me. "Can't your friend pay if you don't have any money?"

"Never mind," Angela said.

Hal stood, and as he pulled up his trousers there was a slight clinking of coins. "Cara, I'm sorry. You know."

"Never mind."

Hal left.

Angela said, "He's a creep."

Drunk, I laughed.

"I don't need the money," she said; "I was just testing him, and he didn't pass the test."

"He wasn't very friendly," I said.

She sat still biting her lower lip. "Come on," she said, "let's go home."

People had to move out of my way as I carried my valise; I bumped it sometimes against them, against the corners of houses in the narrow streets, and scraped it along walls as I tried to stay out of the way. My false soles made me feel I could at any moment lose my balance. Sweating, I kept up with Angela, who walked ahead, looking at everyone, and everyone looked at her.

At a glass door with a metal grille she stopped and searched in a small leather pouch, carried by thongs, for the key. Once she unlocked the door, she gave the key to me. "You keep this one." I put it in my pocket.

Going up the stairs she said, "Hal's really a nice guy. If

he had the money, I know he'd give it to me. I'm sure he would."

She opened the door to the apartment and went in and I went in after her and dropped my valise in the dark hall. When Angela put a light on, I saw the hall was filled with cardboard boxes and paper bags and empty wine bottles.

"Come on in here," Angela said, and she led the way into the living room, which she lighted. It was a large white room, and on all the furniture, the sofa, the armchairs, the dining table and chairs and buffet, were clothes and shoes, and rumpled newspapers, magazines, paperback books. She pulled some dresses off the sofa and said, "Sit here." I sat. My drunkenness swelled up under me, then ebbed. She sat across from me in an armchair, amidst clothes.

"He is a good guy," she said. "I know he is."

I said, "I should have been friendlier with him, maybe he'd have been friendlier with me."

She suddenly saw me. She stood, her hand out. "Come on. I haven't shown you around the apartment."

Her hand in mine, she took me through the rooms.

"It's great, isn't it?" she said. "I'm so lucky."

Her bed was unmade, and tangled in the sheets were clothes; surrounding the bed were trunks, open, and more clothes hung from them. On a bedside table were wigs. There were many shoes on the floor.

The small guest room was bare except for two beds.

In the kitchen, where the table was piled with laundry, stockings and underpants and blouses and brassieres heaped together, she took from a cupboard two glasses and a bottle of wine.

"Have you eaten?" she asked.

"Oh," I said.

"There's nothing to eat here. If you're hungry—"

I hadn't eaten since the day before. "No, I'm fine," I said.

We sat in the living room with glasses of wine, and it occurred to me that I had nothing to say to her, and she seemed to have nothing to say to me. She seemed to be wondering what we had to do with one another.

Suddenly, she said, "Do you want me to show you a dress I bought in Paris before I left?"

"Yes."

She went out. I held the glass of wine. I knew I couldn't swallow it. I held it between my knees so it wouldn't spill, and leaned my head against the sofa back. When she came in, I rose up, a little startled.

Angela was in a long pale dress which swelled out when she turned; the swirling cloth of the long skirt billowed about her bare arms.

"Do you like it?"

"It's wonderful."

"Isn't it? I'm so lucky." She sat. "Are you drunk?"

"Yes."

"Very?"

"I think I am, yes." I put the glass of wine on the floor and slouched back.

She laughed.

I closed my eyes and affected falling asleep.

I did fall asleep, and when I woke I was lying on the sofa, covered by a blanket, my shoes off. Blue light came in through the windows to a balcony. I got up, found the bathroom. I passed Angela's bedroom. The door was open. I peed, and still feeling drunk I walked past her open bedroom door off the passageway, and around the living room.

From her room she called softly, "Are you all right?"

"I'm fine," I said. "I'm really fine."

I waited for her to say more, but she was silent.

In the small guest room, I closed the door, but there was no key in the lock. I got into bed with my underpants on.

2

T H E room was hot and filled with flies. Awake, I watched
the flies. Across the white room from me was an un-
used bed, covered with a sheet. Flies settled on and rose
from the sheet.

I gently lifted my sheet, drew it aside, and stood on the
tile floor. I was sweating. I moved quietly to a chair where
my trousers and tee shirt were. Putting them on, I wondered why I was being quiet; it was as if I didn't want anyone else in the apartment to know that I was there. Barefoot,
I walked up and down the room. White light through the
slats of the shutters streaked the dim air. I went out.

In the living room, sitting on a chair before large shining windows, Angela was in a dressing gown that was slung
low over her shoulders and open between her legs. Steam
was rising from her head. She jerked around to me when I
came into the room, and the dressing gown slipped down
and opened more. In one hand she held a metal instrument,
a thick comb with a black handle, and connected to the
handle was a cord plugged into a socket. She said "Hi," and
ran the comb through her stiff black hair, and, again, steam
rose from her head.

"Hi," I said.

Angela yanked the plug out of the socket by the cord, which she wrapped about the handle; she dropped the comb to the floor. She bit her lower lip. Her body slumped into the chair. She bit her upper lip and held it. Then she sat up, so her robe opened, and she folded it quickly. Her voice, too, sat up. She must have been wondering what to do with me, I who expected so much. "Go get ready."

I hurried.

When I came back to her in the living room, she was wearing narrow white trousers and a white halter, and she was tying her hair tightly into a knot at the top of her head. Her ears were small and fine, and behind them was blue black. She put on a round straw hat.

She asked me to take the water jug; I carried it by the straw handle of the basket which encased the green glass.

Outside, in the small cobbled street, she passed her slim arm through mine and led the way. The doors to the houses were open, and the people standing in the doorways—an old woman, a child in a blue smock, a young man in shorts and an undershirt—stared at Angela and me; sometimes the person in the doorway called others from inside the houses to come and look, and faces appeared, behind grilles. The house fronts were whitewashed, and along all edges, edges of the door jambs, window encasements, corners, were fine blue lines, so the buildings appeared to be flat and given perspective only by the blue lines. Angela and I went by a garage at the bottom of a house in which two men were repairing an old truck, and as we, the strangers, passed, the men whistled. Angela laughed.

"Isn't it wonderful?" she asked.

I didn't know what to say. Talking to her was a little

79

like walking with her; I tried to keep in step with her, but she walked in short, bouncing steps, and I was always out of step. I was very excited, and, in my excitement, I wanted to give over all my senses to Angela, who would spark off each sense with a small shock. Now, I did not consider that Spain was anything but her country, and she knew it all, possessed it all. It was a country where there was no daily living.

I said, "You're getting a lot of attention."

"That's because I'm black," she said.

"It must be strange."

"Strange that I'm black? They think it's strange."

I'd never heard her refer before to being black.

"No, no, that these people don't have any kind of idea what kind of life you—"

"Wait," she said, and she stopped and leaned on me to take off her sandals. She shook loose the string net bag she was carrying and inserted the sandals. "Take your shoes off," she said, and I did as she did. I untied my large shoes, pulled off my socks, put the socks in the shoes, and the shoes in the bag. She noticed the false soles, and laughed, saying, "They get every foreigner." We continued.

"You can leave the water jug at the corner shop there," she said.

I went into the shop thinking: maybe its crazy to go in with the idea that I'm going into this shop for the first time in my life. In their vividness, what would have been to these people everyday objects were not to me, and appeared to stand out from themselves, large and solid. The shop was filled with green bottles encased in straw. There were funnels in some of the bottles. The air inside was cool and smelled fresh, and there was a sound of running water. I gave the water jug to a girl, who, holding it by the two handles, followed me back to the door. I turned round to her to nod and thank her again, but she was looking out the door, past me. Across the road, standing against the white wall of the garden, was Angela. A woman and two men, one man with a wooden wheelbarrow, had stopped to look at her. Angela raised a foot behind her to rest it against the wall, and she spread out her arms and long fingers. I hesitated. As I advanced toward her, she smiled. I held out my arm to her, and the others went on.

I felt the wheel ruts and worn cobbles of the dry hot streets against my soles. The street was half in shadow; we walked in the sun. Sometimes we had to separate to avoid the donkey droppings. We turned up a narrower steep street. I blinked, passing often from sunlight to shadow, from shadow to sunlight; in the sunlight the walls appeared solid, and in shadow they appeared black space; and then the appearances shifted, and the shadows were solid, the white light open space.

In the market, these blinding shifts made me uncertain where I was. I followed close behind Angela, across the square and into the market, its metal roof supported by thin iron pillars.

"Look," Angela said, "look." She did not know which way to go, and tried, I thought, to go in all directions. She pointed. "Look. Just look."

Against black solidity or black space, or against white-blankness or white openness, shifting as often as I blinked, I saw melons on the steps of the market piled on burlap sacks, olives in baskets, grapes heaped on tables with scales by them, strings of peppers and onions hanging from the iron scrolls about the pillars.

Angela rubbed her nose; her nose was as small and rounded as a child's. As she rubbed her nose, I followed her around the pavilion, from counters to chopping blocks. On the chopping blocks were great hunks of meat, where flies collected and dispersed. Blood drained down the sides of the blocks. On the counters were the innards of pigs and sheep: brains and tripe, hocks and lungs, livers, kidneys, hearts in blood-filled basins. Hogs' heads hung from iron hooks. I noticed a woman shopper stop to stare and another, by her, lean towards her, raise her hand to her mouth, and speak. This woman smiled at Angela, and Angela half smiled back; the staring woman smiled too. As Angela and I approached a counter a woman held out to us a chunk of meat; the blood oozed between her fingers. Angela said something in Spanish. A man came up behind the woman, took the meat from her, and held it out to Angela. He said something in Spanish, his voice eager. I caught the man with the meat look at me as if to ask who I was with this strange woman.

"No," Angela said.

Around the market we came to the fish stall. On a table inside the stall was a small shark lying on its side in a tub of water. The air smelled of fish, of seaweed. On the tilted marble slab were two fish. Angela bought one of these. The woman, all the time staring at Angela, wrapped the fish in paper and handed it across to her. Angela opened the bag and rested it on her sandals and my shoes, then reached into her pocket for peseta bills folded in half.

"No," I said, "I'm paying." I took my wallet out.

Angela said, "Look, you've got to tell me—do you have money?"

"Not a lot," I said, "no, but—"

"Then I'll pay."

"You can't."

"I will."

I didn't put my wallet back, but held it in my hand.

In the center of the market were stalls with bulging bags of dried beans, peas, rice. I followed Angela to a fruit stall where she bought half a kilo of plums and a half a kilo of apricots. As if embarrassed, the young woman, placing the fruit in paper cones and folding the tops of the cones over, kept her eyes down; Angela held open the net bag close to her so she could put the cones in without looking up, and she didn't look up, either, when Angela paid her.

I slipped my wallet into my back pocket when Angela turned away.

Shoppers stepped aside to let Angela and me go by. I thought: she is aware of them staring at her, all with the wonder that a person could be so black. She skipped a little as she walked. She kept touching her neck, forehead, ears.

In the square, we passed an old woman selling socks from a cardboard box on the ground, and an old man selling rusted keys laid out on a piece of canvas. The old man went rigid when he saw Angela and me, who walked, I behind her, to a corner of the square, where, in shade, a man was selling watermelons. The man picked up a watermelon into the crook of his arm and raised a knife in his right hand. But Angela walked away from him, towards a man sitting on a low stool by a row of flowers in tin cans. The flowers were in sunlight against the wall. Angela bought roses and irises. She held the bouquet in her arm so the blossoms were against her shoulder. She passed along the bright white wall, then into the shadow of a street.

A little girl, standing against a wall, seemed about to

shout at the sudden sight of Angela, but she clapped her hands over her mouth and turned away and pressed herself against the wall. Angela apparently didn't care. It was as if she was excited that she could shock. As we passed the little girl, she turned to us, and flat against the wall, her eyes wide, said something to Angela, and Angela laughed.

"What did she say?" I asked.

She said, "She wants to know if I'm in mourning."

Here, Angela enjoyed her self-consciousness.

At a corner, we turned into the sun. I had to turn my eyes away from the white brightness.

She said, "Let's take the long way back to the house."

We continued in the direction of the sun and came out, suddenly, on the sea and the sky.

Before the bright black sea and black sky, I began to think: No, I have never seen—

Angela said, "Come on."

Stumbling, I went after her. We passed the cafés, with tables and chairs outside, along the sea front. Across the road before the cafés was the beach, and, beyond the beach, the sea and sky. The road ended at rocks. A narrow street to the right went back up into town.

Angela said, "The water jug."

Dazed, I picked up the water jug by its straw handles; it tipped, and a little water spilled out. I thought: why am I so lightheaded? I waited while Angela bought five bright eggs.

Angela asked me, "Don't you like anything?"

We were approaching the door to the apartment house. "What?"

"You haven't said anything."

Going up the stairs, I said, "I've been talking all the time, haven't I?"

In the bathroom, I looked at myself in the mirror over the wash basin: eyes, the irises large, in a thin face. There was no expression in that face. To react, I would have to react to everything at once, all together, and what reaction could that be?

3

EACH morning, Angela said she'd think of something terrific for us to do that day. She was, however, waiting for something else to happen, more important than anything she could think up to do; she was always thinking of something else.

I tried to take the false soles off my shoes with a bottle opener, but couldn't. After a while I got used to them. From time to time, I was reminded of them when I'd trip.

Most of the time we sat around in the apartment. We drew pictures of the views from the windows. We ate cooked beans, bread and cheese, and we drank wine.

One afternoon, I bought in a small shop near the market a light pullover shirt, light trousers which billowed from the waist to the crotch, and a pair of sandals.

For a moment, alone with her in the apartment, I thought I would ask Angela about her life in America, because I could not imagine her there, the city where she was born, her neighborhood, her house, and then it occurred to me: don't.

She had never asked me about my life in America.

Here, abroad, we were not from separate cities, neighborhoods, houses. We were, though we were as different as black and white from one another, both Americans.

She stopped and raised the back of a hand and looked at it, and then she rubbed it with the index finger of her other hand. She frowned, dropping her hand, and continued to walk.

She must have been thinking about the man she'd come to Spain for.

He might suddenly open the door and appear, and sometimes I imagined he was, invisible, already in the apartment.

My third day with Angela, it rained. The daylight passed into dark. The glass doors to the balcony open, rain fell inside from the dark night and with the rain came the smell of the sea. On the glass doors were reflected, in the dim electric light, parts of the room; and Angela, on a sofa, and me, in an armchair, were, in the reflections, extended at different angles out into the night and the rain.

Angela got up. She walked around the room, pulling her hair straight. Then she said, "I know what we'll do. We'll buy more wine."

Quickly, lightly, she stepped up and down and shook her shoulders and her hands. "Let's go," she said, "Let's go, let's get going, let's get going, let's go, let's go, let's go." She held one arm against her waist, and the other out; snapping the fingers of one hand, she moved, in light steps of two forward and one back, across the floor to the door.

In the small entrance hall, I took from a big jar an umbrella. "We don't need that," Angela said. She undid her sandals and threw them into a corner. I took off my sandals and rolled up my trousers. Angela gave me an empty bottle and kept one.

The rain streaked in the dim light about the street lamps

fixed to the houses, there was no sound but the falling rain and the rush of water down the central gutter of the stone paved street. With her empty bottle, Angela ran ahead. She disappeared in the darkness reappeared in the lamp light, and turned to find me. She contorted her face to see through the drops hitting and running down her cheeks, nose, chin.

My shoulders hunched, I ducked under a balcony, stood for a moment, then ran to the next balcony. My feet splashed the water.

Angela whispered, "Let's go."

I rushed past her and continued up the hill to where the rain was illuminated by a small shop window. The fly straps over the doorway flew out when I, unable to stop, rushed into the shop, my bottle held out. The proprietor, a man sitting on a tun and reading a paper in the electric light, stood when Angela came in.

The proprietor filled our bottles with a funnel from a tun. He stuffed rolls of newspaper into the bottle necks. Angela did her two steps forward and one step back dance in the shop on the dirt floor, among the tuns and bottles. She shook water from her head. The proprietor pretended not to see her. I stood back, in a shadow.

As we returned, thunder sounded from the sea; with the thunder the street lamps flickered.

I slipped on a smooth wet paving stone, and for a moment, one leg and an arm out, kept my balance. Angela, by me, grabbed the bottle of wine from my hand and I fell backwards onto my behind. She ran ahead with the two bottles, and I ran after her, down the hill, through narrow streets, and out to the sea front. Beyond the lights from the cafés a pale light appeared and disappeared on the sea; then there was thunder. Angela, her arms out, jumped from the sea wall and onto the dark beach. I jumped after her. The rain, in the open, fell on us in waves. We ran in it to the surf. Angela stuck the bottles in the sand, just beyond where the surf reached, and began to undress. As she undressed she ran from me to the other side of the beach; I saw her throw off her clothes and become invisible. Only when the light flashed across the sea did she appear, walking against the surf into the sea.

It was as if we were enjoying ourselves before it would no longer be possible, as though we would soon not be allowed to enjoy ourselves.

I was free.

Facing away from the cafés, I pulled off my shirt and trousers and underpants. As I ran across the beach, I felt my erection hit my thigh; my body was hot. I dived in. The rain on the sea hissed. My body felt solid and round in the water. I let myself sink and I swam under the water, where I could see nothing, and when I rose I still saw nothing. I turned and spotted, over a rising and falling blackness, lights. I swam away from the lights. Flashes illuminated the waves. I thought: go back to shore, go back and go away. At a distance out, I swam along the shore; not I, but it rose and fell in the lightning flashes.

There was no more lightning, and I headed towards the shore; I swam for a long time, expecting at any moment to touch the bottom with a foot, but every time I pressed a foot down I sank in deeply and had to rise because I lost my breath. The rain beat against my eyes as I tried to look.

In a long white flash I saw Angela standing at the edge of the sea, naked; I saw in her, in the slim body of the black woman at the edge of the sea, the spirit to make anything happen.

89

The whole world seemed to me to open up when I emerged from the sea. I stretched out my arms in the rain; I wanted my body to remain, forever, naked, and in its nakedness sensitive not just to this or that, but to everything. I wanted everything. My arms still out, I walked over the wet sand towards Angela.

She was sitting on the beach, her legs were drawn up, and she was holding her knees. When I crouched before her, she kept her body closed up.

She said, "You shouldn't be with me. You should go away."

I rose and walked away from her. I went along the beach for my sodden clothes and the bottles of wine. Wearing only the wet trousers, I returned to her. She was dressed, and her clothes stuck to her. I shivered. The lightning and the thunder came together, so the light crashed, the sound flashed.

Angela said, "We'd better get back."

On the way, we were silent. The bottles held by their necks in one hand, I dragged my shirt in the other.

Dripping, I waited in the stark entry to the apartment for Angela to come with a large towel, which she held open.

She said softly, "Turn around."

My back to her, she placed the towel over my shoulders, and rubbed it against me. I felt her hands press the towel under my arms, which I raised. As she rubbed the towel down my spine, to my buttocks, I held my breath. I didn't want her to touch me, and yet there I stood while she softly rubbed my body warm.

"Turn back," she said quietly, as if she were tired.

Her eyes unfocused, she dried my neck, my ears, and I lowered my head for her to dry my hair. She dried my chest, and I held in my stomach; when the towel slipped and her fingers met my skin, I jolted. Her eyes were not focused on any part of me, but she seemed to be seeing me altogether, as in a blur. She drew back, the towel, held by her at the corners, hanging in folds. I made myself say, "Give me the towel. I'll dry you."

The towel in my hands, I hesitated, then I wrapped it about her upper body and with the corners rubbed her hair, which swelled out into a soft mass. I did not want to do this. I made myself take an edge of the towel and wipe her neck, her jaw, her cheeks, and as I did it occurred to me that her blackness, if I rubbed harder, would come off. I would find she was, under, not black, but a color I could not have expected: not white, but blue. As I rubbed her face, she twisted it up and away. I rubbed the back of her neck, and held her to me, then I let her go. Angela began to unbutton her wet shirt so I could continue to dry her, and I watched her for a moment, watched until I saw the inner sides of her black breasts, and I held the towel out to her.

I whispered, "I guess you'd better continue."

Her hands fell from her shirt and she looked at me. Her shoulder and hips, too, fell.

"All right," she said.

She left me holding the towel.

In my bedroom, changing, I thought: I must go away from here—

My fresh clothes felt like a second skin, even more sensitive than my warm dry skin. I wanted to stay in my room, and sat on the edge of my bed. But after a while I went out.

Rain fell through the open glass doors. The tile floor was wet. I stood just outside the rain falling inside.

Angela came into the living room wearing a long narrow dress, and she walked about as if she were alone. There was pain in her face. She frowned. She walked from point to point, wandering. When she reached a wall, she touched it and turned away to continue to wander.

She went past me, out onto the balcony. I remained where I was, but in the reflection on a glass door I could see her standing and looking at the dark mountain. When she came back into the living room she went to the sofa and sat at an end, and she put a hand to her forehead.

She said to me, her voice strained, "I was thinking we could climb that mountain."

The lights in the room flickered.

Angela got up from the sofa and came towards me, and I stepped back. I felt the rain on my nape. Her hands hanging loosely at her sides, she stood before me. I was embarrassed, because I suddenly imagined that Angela was pretending, though I was not sure what. The fact was I could not believe that Angela was not false. A flash illuminated the room, and after it the room was dark. I heard Angela move away from me. At the other side of the room a candle was lit, and the light of the candle was blown by drafts. She sat at the end of the sofa, her legs under her. As if she were alone, she touched her face, her neck, her shoulders. I sat across from her on a chair.

She said, as if speaking to herself, "Tomorrow, I'm going into the city."

"Can't I go with you?"

She didn't answer.

The tips of my fingers and my toes were cold. My body felt drawn in and tight and cold, as if in water.

"Can I?" I asked.

"You can do what you like."

"There should be a lot to see."

"There's a lot to see."

"Maybe you can show me."

"I don't know if you'd want to see what I have to show you."

"Oh I—," I said, and stopped.

Staring vaguely beyond me, Angela bit a knuckle; then her eyes focused and she sat at the edge of the sofa and said, "Look," and pointed behind me. I turned round to the wide open glass doors, but saw nothing; then I heard hands clap, and I turned back to her. She was standing, smiling; she lifted in turn her bare feet from the tiles, jutted out her shoulders and pulled them in, extended and retracted her fine neck, and snapped the fingers of her wrist-loose hands as she hummed. She revolved slowly, and each time she turned to me she smiled.

I smiled back.

The electric lights came on, and Angela hid her eyes.

"Shut them off," she said.

I jumped up and switched them off.

"Where're those bottles of wine?" she asked.

I rushed out to the kitchen for them and brought both back, one tucked under each arm, and clean glasses in my hands. I poured.

"Can I come into the city with you?" I asked.

"You can come in with me."

Angela emptied a glass and held it up. I drank down my glass. The rough wine made me shudder.

Angela said, "Oh, I forgot to tell you."

"Yes?"

"You'll have to let me have some money to get into Barcelona."

I hesitated. "Of course," I said, "sure."

In my room, I counted my cash and traveler's checks, then hid them in my dirty underwear.

4

ANGELA hailed a taxi outside the train station in Barcelona. A ship was coming into the harbor between long low buildings and palm trees. The taxi went down the wide avenue along the port and round a monument: statutes of lions, eagles, and wreath-holding angels about the base, and on the top of a column a giant, pointing. I pressed my forehead against the glass to see up the monument.

"Who is that?" I asked.

"Christopher Columbus," Angela said.

The taxi took us up the Ramblas Generalissimo Franco, where people walked along a broad promenade under trees.

Angela looked intently out the window on her side.

We got out in a square. The late sunlight was against one side of the square, and, under the arched arcade, made another arcade of shadows. I followed Angela closely through the arcades of stone and shadow to the entrance of a club. The neon sign above the entrance was off.

Angela kept swallowing nervously, looking back at me from time to time as we went down frayed carpeted stairs, past the coat check where, on a shelf, was a saucer and a roll of tickets. The club was beneath street level; in the light which came through high barred windows the basement room was gray. There was an acrid smell. Around a corner table were a woman and two men. One of the men was Hal. The other tables were empty, and chairs were turned upside down on them. Angela stopped for a moment, then went towards the group, but I stayed behind. They waited till she was near and greeted her in an offhand way in Spanish. She stood by their table. In the seated group, the woman delicately touched her hair, which was piled up high, with ringlets across her forehead. Her face looked swollen. The man I didn't know was tall and gaunt. Angela talked mostly with him; she seemed to be having an argument with him, which Hal listened to silently. As she talked, her voice rising, she often licked her lips as if to keep them from sticking together, and she pointed to herself. The tall gaunt man said in English, "All right, all right." Angela continued to argue. He said, "All right, I tell you." He was Spanish. Angela frowned.

Hal nodded his head towards me and said, "You came with your friend."

Angela seemed to have forgotten, and she stared at me for a moment. "My friend?" she said.

In a low voice, the tall man asked something in Spanish. Angela answered, in Spanish, in a low voice. The tall man glanced at me, said something more, and Angela made a gesture to me to come over. She kept licking her lips as she introduced the Spaniard, Miguel. He turned over and over a packet of cigarettes on the table. The woman pursed her lips. Hal got up and held out his hand; his trousers dropped a little from about his waist with the noise of loose change.

I noted that across the Spaniard's forehead was a straight thin scar. Hal brought more chairs to the table.

Angela said, "Hal, I didn't notice, you've lost weight."

"All my clothes are getting too big for me."

"Why're you losing?"

"I'm losing everything."

"You need money?" Angela said. "I'll give you some money." She opened her purse.

"No, no," he said.

"I can give you this." She held out the bill.

I did not know if it was the money I had given to her.

"No, no."

"Sure?"

"All right," he said. He reached for it. "I'll pay you back tomorrow."

Miguel said to Angela, "If you're lucky."

The woman with the swollen face yawned. Miguel spoke to her harshly in Spanish and she quickly covered her yawn with the back of her hand.

The hundred peseta bill between his fingers, Hal said to me, "How about a drink?"

I said, "Let me buy you all a drink."

"Never mind," Angela said

"I wouldn't mind a drink," Hal said.

Miguel said, "If he wants to buy us drinks, why shouldn't he?"

"Because he doesn't have the money to buy people drinks," Angela said.

Miguel spoke in Spanish to the woman, who got up and went into a back room.

As if she knew she were making an impossible request,

Angela asked Miguel, "So if Vincent doesn't come in any more, where does he go?"

Miguel picked up the pack of cigarettes and dropped it. "You ask me?"

She looked about. "This place hasn't changed." She made a face as of tasting something sour.

"You expect anything to change?" Miguel said.

The woman, her swollen face expressionless, came to the table with a shining bucket; from the bucket a bottle stuck up. She placed it before Miguel. While he undid the wires around the cork she went for glasses, which she put on the table. Miguel poured.

He leaned across the table and said to me in a quiet voice, "You like Spain?"

"Yes," I said.

Hal said to me, "Stay. Do what I did and stay." He patted me on the back.

I put my elbows on the table. I said, smiling, "I'd like that."

Miguel laughed a little; the scar across his forehead wrinkled. "You're all right," he said, and he reached out to touch my wrist.

While the others drank, Angela didn't, but scratched her twitching nose and appeared to search the empty club room. Everyone was attentive to her.

Miguel said, "Why don't you stay away from Vincent? Stay away from him."

Angela became aware of me. She said quickly to me, "Let's go out." She stood.

Hal stood. "I'll come with you. Where're you going? I can show you a few places."

I walked close to Angela's side under the arcade. Hal was on her other side. He talked in a small bright high voice. At the end of the arcade was a café, with painted metal tables and chairs. As soon as we sat, Hal said, "Excuse me for a second," and got up and went out into the square to a man standing by a palm tree. I watched everything. His eyes half closed, the man by the palm tree slowly shook his head as Hal spoke to him. Hal began to use his hands as he talked, and made a fist of one to hit the other. The man shook his head.

Angela said, "I'd better go."

Hal stepped back as she took his place to talk to the man by the palm tree. She was dressed like a business woman in a two piece double-breasted tan suit, the skirt just below her knees, and she had on white high heeled shoes. The man listened to her, his eyes half closed, but his head still.

Angela took Hal's arm as they came towards the table, and when they sat she said, "Forget it, Hal. Forget it." Her face was screwed up as if against smoke.

"Sure," he said.

"What the hell," she said, "it's only life."

Hal sat up. He smiled at the glasses of beer being carried to the table on a round tin tray. He held out a plump hand for one.

Angela put her glass on the table. She tried to appear as if she were concentrating on what was happening in the plaza and on nothing else; but she wasn't able to carry off the outward act, because when she said to Hal, as if it had just occurred to her, "So Vincent hasn't been doing any jobs lately?" I knew that she'd been told this by Miguel, and that it had struck her in a way to worry her.

99

"Did I say that?" Hal asked.

"Maybe not. Maybe Miguel did. But you know as much about him as anybody else, except you don't want to say."

"No. I don't know anything about Vincent."

"You do."

"No, I don't," Hal said. "And neither do you."

"Forget about it," Angela said.

"All right." Hal drank some beer.

"I asked you to forget it."

"All right. I've forgotten about it."

Angela said, "I do know him."

"If you ask me," Hal said turning to me, "it's no wonder he has breakdowns."

"I see," I said, nodding.

"You don't know anything about him," Angela said to Hal. "You don't know anything about his breakdowns."

"And you do? You know what causes them? Well, maybe you do."

"No," Angela said, "I don't."

Hal leaned towards her. He said, "So what is it? You came back hoping to do another job with Vincent? You came back because you need to make some money?"

Angela crossed her arms and legs.

Hal said, "I do know how he's been, if you want to know. He's been quiet these six months since you left. It's as if he decided, like he decides everything, to stop doing any jobs." His empty glass in his hand, he leaned towards her and spoke quietly. "He's quiet. Let him be."

"I know Vincent," Angela said. "I know he can't be quiet."

"You shouldn't have taken all the money and gone away."

"I didn't come back to get more money."

"I somehow don't think you came back to give him what you took. Why did you come back?"

Angela said nothing. She kept crossing and uncrossing her legs, crossing and uncrossing her arms, twisting her fingers together and untwisting them. I sat still, but I felt my body, inside, was moving as Angela's moved; I finally got up and walked out into the soft darkness of the square. Some windows were lit and shone onto the palm trees.

Angela called, "Where're you going?"

"Nowhere."

Spanish voices resonated about the square.

Restless, I walked to an illuminated kiosk in the square and studied the postcards in a rack. I took out a postcard depicting the square: under an arcade were small tables and chairs and a few people were sitting at the tables, and beyond the arches of the arcade were palm trees, and beyond the palm trees the windows of the building across. The picture looked as though it had been taken twenty years before, and was black and white. On the reverse was printed: Plaza Real/Place Real/Real Square. I bought it and put it in the pocket of my sports shirt.

People were gathered at the tables of the café. The pavement was littered with the shells and heads of shrimps, bottle caps, butts. Hal was drinking beer, and Angela was staring at her hands; she splayed out her fingers, brought them together, splayed them far out again. She rubbed her skin.

I sat beside her and said quietly, "Let's do something. Let's see something."

"What?"

"Let's walk around."

Angela stood, "Come on, then."

Under the arms of Angela's suit were dark stains. In the lights we passed her face gleamed. Along the Ramblas, people kept turning to look at her and a man carrying a canary in a cage whistled at her. She looked beyond these people for someone else, just beyond the people around them. Hal, behind, talked, but to no one. Angela led us into a street on the other side of the Ramblas, a narrow cobbled street, which gave into narrower cobbled streets, which gave into dirt alleys. I found myself walking as Angela walked, turning, in small jerks of her body, in many directions, and sometimes stepping backwards or to the side. How could I take in all the cobbles, the street lamps, the doorways, the bird cages outside windows, the fire escapes, the cast-iron fountains at corners? Take them in and, somehow, preserve them, because I had the strange sense that everything I saw was doomed.

Perhaps, I thought, I should have stayed in France. Perhaps I shouldn't have come to another country.

A child came out of an open doorway, stopped short when he saw Angela, and stared at her with large eyes; when Angela moved on, he followed at a distance. Passing a doorway, he called to two more children leaning on the jambs, and they joined him. Angela kept turning around, and each time she turned she stopped, myself with her, so Hal, his head lolling as he talked to himself, went ahead of us. A group of boys and girls formed, and when Angela turned and stopped, they, too, stopped, and they pushed one another. Angela seemed to look over their heads. When Angela went towards them they stepped back. A little girl, in sandals and a torn dress, spoke, and put her hand to her dirty mouth. Angela spoke. The little girl reached out and grabbed Angela's skirt and pulled, and the other children surrounded her, and as I watched she was brought by the shifting little group across the street, alongside a shop, and into a narrow street. I thought she would come out, and, waiting, watched a woman feed seeds to a canary in a cage on the wall outside the shop. Hal came up to me.

"Where is she?" Hal asked.

"I'd better go get her," I said.

I went into the street; the buildings appeared to tilt out over it, and I walked through the tilting shadows cast by the lamps on the walls. I couldn't see Angela, and I looked into side streets and open doorways. The street ended. I turned at the corner and continued. There were many cages along the walls, and birds chirped in them. I turned another corner, and when I realized I was lost I stopped in fear. I did not want to be alone in this city. Behind me, she called me, and I turned and hurried to her; she was standing outside a doorway, and the children were crushed together just inside.

"What happened?" I asked.

"They wanted to show me something."

"What?"

Her eyes had shifting points of light in them, and I knew she was waiting for me to ask, again, what it was; but I saw that she wouldn't tell me, not because she didn't want me to know, but because she knew the sense of it was greater that what it itself could be; I saw this in her eyes.

She touched my head.

"We'd better get back to Hal," she said.

As the three of us continued through the streets, Angela kept looking into the open doorways, windows, arched passageways. From time to time, her high heels wobbling in the spaces between the cobbles, she held on to me.

We paused at a café and she looked in. Its ceiling was low and the floor was earth.

She said to me, "You don't want to know what the kids showed me?"

"No," I said.

She laughed. She said, "I'll show you something."

"What?"

"I'll find it first."

I took her hand as we went on.

Angela stopped before the open door of an apartment house. Past a staircase and a passage with a broken bicycle was a courtyard illuminated by a bare bulb; at rickety tables men were sitting and drinking and watching a very fat woman dance. The woman held one arm across her waist, and the other up; she stood in one spot and, lifting her feet a little, shifted her body, and the man shouted, "Olé."

Angela said, "Let's go in there."

"In there?"

"You don't want to?"

"Yes," I said, "yes, let's go."

Hal said, "Hey, where're you going?"

Angela pointed. "In there."

She led the way.

The fat woman, dancing, closed her eyes when we came into the courtyard. There was no music. A man got up quickly from a table and held one hand out to us, another to a table.

We ordered cognac.

"This is going to be expensive," Hal said.

"Shut up," Angela said. She touched my hand. "Look," she said.

On the edge of her chair, she watched the fat woman. In a loose waistless dress which, with sweat, stuck to her body, the woman danced with slow, then quick, movements; slow to raise a foot, quick to strike it down; slow to raise her arms, quick to bend back her wrists and clap her small hands, and there were long moments when she was tensely still. Her head was raised, her eyes shut, the corners of her mouth turned down, and she was frowning; she appeared about to weep. Angela, watching her, didn't move. The fat dancing woman remained still for a long moment, and there was a stillness, too, in the courtyard, the stillness of an unbearably acute awareness, then she simply lowered her arms, opened her eyes, and walked to a table and joined some men who began to play dice.

Angela turned to me. I nodded.

"How about a game of craps?" Hal said.

Angela kept looking at the space where the woman had danced.

"How about it?" Hal said.

He called to the man who had served us for dice and the bottle of cognac.

"Should I?" I asked Angela.

"Do what you want," she said.

I didn't want to play after that woman's dance. But Hal and I rolled the dice again and again over the metal table top. I won over and over, and each time I won Hal said, "How about that?" and each time his voice went lower.

Angela became attentive to the game. She asked Hal, "How much do you owe him?"

Hal said to me, "How much do I owe you? I haven't been keeping a record."

"Nothing."

"Yes, he does," Angela said.

"No," I said, "nothing."

"He'd take from you everything you had if he won."

"I guess I would," Hal said. He laughed. "I guess I would."

"Give me an IOU," I said.

"For how much?"

"Make it an even thousand pesetas," Angela said.

"A thousand?" Hal took an old restaurant bill from his pocket and with a pencil wrote on the back of it. He gave it to me. "That's almost hard currency," he said.

Putting the paper in the pocket of my short-sleeved shirt, I said to Angela, "I never played before."

Hal hit me on the head and poured out for me another glass of cognac, then poured out for Angela and himself.

Drinking, I wanted to get up and move. I went still when I saw the fat woman's face among the men's faces at her table, in the light from the bare bulb.

Angela said, "We'd better get back to the club."

On the Ramblas, two young men followed behind Angela and me. Hal now walked ahead. Angela often turned to look, it appeared, beyond the young men, who stopped when she stopped, and, themselves, turned round to look. One of the young men called out, "Ay, negrita."

Angela fell back, and I with her. She went to the side of the Ramblas where, under a tree, were wire cages piled up, and in the cages puppies barked. The puppies were jumping and yapping; sometimes they stopped to bite their rumps, then they jumped and yapped more. A man with a beret stood behind the cages. The crisscrossing wires of the metal cages gleamed in the electric light. For a long while Angela and I stared at the dogs. Then Angela turned, and I did.

Walking, Angela asked me, "What's wrong with you?"

"I didn't think there was anything wrong," I said.

"You seem restless."

I laughed.

"Tell me what's wrong," Angela said. "I feel there's something wrong."

"Yes," I said, "I'm restless."

Then she said, "You want everything."

And I said, "I'll get it."

5

THE neon sign over the entrance to the club was lit.
In the dim light of the club I sat with Angela at a table;
she was attentive to me as I, in her attention, tossed up,
over and over, a ball of foil from a champagne bottle over
the snout of a puppy, which jumped up, over and over, to
try to snap it in its teeth. We were waiting. I suddenly threw
the ball of foil to Angela; she jolted, but caught it, and
threw it back to me over the head of the puppy, which, wag-
ging every part in its excitement, jumped from one to the
other.

A man in a trim suit came through the door and over
to the table. Angela stopped playing with the dog and me.
When I threw the ball of foil to Angela, it fell to the floor.

The tendons stood out in Angela's thin neck. With an
expression of terror in her eyes, as if what the man might
do, she, still tensed, watched him come closer and take a
chair next to her. She drew her body back. His back straight,
his shoulders square, he sat, his face stark. He slouched forward, and as he appeared to fall, slowly, toward her, he
closed his eyes. She turned sideways, away from him. His
forehead rested on her left shoulder. Angela, too, closed her

eyes. Her right hand rose, and she held it above his head; it remained there. He opened his eyes. Angela was still, her hand raised above his head.

He said, "You shouldn't have come back."

Angela opened her eyes and dropped her hand to her lap, but she didn't say anything.

He sat up. "Why did you?" he asked.

She cocked her head to the side and she tried to smile, but she was, I saw, frightened. Perhaps she didn't know what to say. Her voice high, she said, "I wondered if you'd take me on a job." Her voice broke.

His face set with a frown. "A job?"

She moved, as if changing her position, however slightly, would change their talk. "Vincent, I don't have any money—"

He said, "You know me. Don't you think you took a chance in coming back?"

"I know how you feel and think about me."

Heavily, he said, "You shouldn't count too much on what I think and feel. You'd better pay me what you took from me."

"Come on, Vincent, don't play with me," Angela said. "Be serious with me. Help me with a job."

"Pay me back the money you took from me, and you can have me to kill, if you want, and I won't care. But I'm going to get my money."

"I don't know where to begin to do a job. You know I don't."

The man stood. "You get the money—"

"All right. I know. I know."

The puppy was yelping. Angela picked it up and gave it to its owner, a woman at the next table.

She said to me, "Look, I've got work to do. You couldn't go somewhere for a hour or so, could you?"

My eyes were wide. "Go where?"

"You wouldn't like to go out into the city and wander around? I could draw you a map," she said, "so you wouldn't get lost."

"All right," I said.

"Or you can go to a restaurant, the restaurant in the square. Aren't you hungry?"

"Aren't you?"

"No, not now."

"But I won't know what to order."

"I'll tell you what to order. I'll write it out."

She didn't introduce me to the man, but in his presence I felt he could do whatever he wanted to me.

At a table covered by a white cloth in the restaurant in the square, I sat under a big framed sepia photograph of the square with horses and carriages in it.

I wanted to be a criminal.

I left some pesetas on the saucer and bumped against empty tables on my way out. As I was opening the glass door with a white curtain stretched over it, a waiter tapped me on a shoulder. I had not left enough money. Bowing to apologize, I gave him another bill; the waiter, smiling, bowed to me. Now, in the city, I did everything wrong.

Many of the tables in the club were circles with dark groups of people. I walked about them to Angela's table. I took a chair next to her. She was looking at Vincent, who looked towards, but not at, a white light which went up on the platform and into which came a woman in a tight blue bathing costume with veils of lighter and darker shades of blue attached to her shoulders and wrists; the veils billowed behind her as she walked to the middle of the platform, then sank when she stopped, faced the audience, and lowered her eyes. She wore a blue cap, tight about her blond hair, and on top of it were wires, glittering blue, arranged like water jets. She lifted her arms, and the streaks flowed. Her arms out, she walked slowly to a corner of the platform, turned, and suddenly stuck a leg out behind her, and held the pose. Both feet on the floor, she swooped down, so the veils were drawn in about her, and she stared up into the lights. The wires on her headdress shook as she held the pose. In quick movements, she strode about the platform and took poses, shaking her blue veils to make them flow like water. There were diamonds cut out of her costume and through them her flesh showed. In all her poses, her body was stiff with self-consciousness. When she bowed, there was little clapping.

Staring above heads, she came to the table where Angela sat. Vincent got up from his chair, gave it to her, and went round the table to sit on the other side of me. He made me think I shouldn't look at him.

Angela said, "You were great, Carole."

I knew that everything Angela said, everything she did, she said and did knowing that Vincent was listening, looking. And though he did not seem to look at me, I wanted to make some little gesture to make him, and was frightened that he would.

His hair was dark, with one grey patch over an ear. There were small wrinkles around his eyes, and the rest of his face was taut, his cheek bones high. He sat leaning away from the chair back, his large hands on his knees.

Carole sat with us. She spread her legs open and leaned over, her elbows on her knees. "Was I?" her voice was a hoarse whisper. She was English. "You didn't see anyone trying to get my eye, did you?"

"I didn't, honey."

"You didn't even notice one you could point out to me to go chat up?"

"Have a drink and forget about it," Angela said.

Carole's eyebrows tilted. "How can I forget it? I need the money by tomorrow morning."

"Look, next time you go on, pick out someone and keep your eyes on him."

"I can't. I get frightened when I look out."

Two tall women on very high heels passed the table; they were arm in arm. They walked slowly among the tables.

Carole sighed. "Whores," she said.

"If you would only learn to get your act across," Angela said, "you wouldn't have anything to worry about, ever—"

I said to Carole, "Your act was wonderful."

"You really mean it?" she asked.

"Yes."

"Sincerely?"

"Yes."

"That's very kind."

I glanced to my side at Vincent, who was looking at me.

Carole held her hands to the sides of her face. After a while she said, "I'd better go see what I can do," and she stumbled a little leaving.

Angela appeared isolated in the attention of Vincent.

I didn't know if I was doing what was right for her, but I said to her, "Would you like to dance?"

She turned her eyes to me without turning her head.

"Will you?" I asked.

She said to Vincent, "I'm going to dance," and he said nothing.

On the dance floor, among other couples who did not dance so much as, in one anothers' arms, step from one foot to the other, I put my arms round Angela and pulled her to me as to protect her. My hand wrinkled the back of her jacket. I took a quick step in reverse and she lurched forward. "I'm sorry," I said. She shook her head a little and put her arms around me; she rested her head on my shoulder, and I felt her breath on my neck.

"You're tired," I said.

"Maybe."

My body, in contact with her, was stiff, and I could not loosen it. I tried to hold her more gently.

At my ear, she said, "I am tired."

"Then we should go home."

"I can't," she said.

I didn't ask her why.

Then she whispered, "How much money do you have?"

Whispering too, I said, "On me?"

"At home."

Quickly, I said, "Not much."

"How much?"

I hesitated.

"You don't want to say?"

"I'm trying to add it up," I said, and then, abruptly, I said, "About two-thousand dollars," and I felt, all at once, I had told her everything about myself that I had not wanted to tell, that I'd wanted to keep a secret to myself.

All my money had been given to me by my brother Albert. It was money which he had earned in the Marine Corps.

She said, "Will you give it to me?"

"Give you all my money?"

"Yes."

"And what will I do?"

I felt her breath on my neck.

I said, "I can't take the risk of having no money."

She drew away from me so I saw her black eyes. She said "Yes, I understand."

"If I—"

"I understand."

She put her forehead against my cheek.

"Is it for him?" I asked.

"Yes," she said.

Vincent sat, his arms crossed, on a chair pulled out from and facing away from the table. I held Angela more closely. Angela and I were not dancing, but standing together, our arms about one another; her face was warm and sweaty against the side of my face.

I asked, "Shouldn't we get back to him?"

"Let's go sit at the bar for a drink first."

At the bar, I stood so I could see him.

Looking at herself in the mirror behind the glass shelves of bottles, Angela dragged her long fingers across her cheeks, pulling at her face and distorting her nose and lips.

"What is it?" I asked.

She was against a light behind the bar; the beams radiated about her, and from the center of the beams she reached out and touched me. All about me, the voices in the club rose loud and sank back, again and again, and among the voices I heard Angela say quietly, "Give me the money."

As if she held a gun up to me, I held up my arms. "Are you daring me?" I asked.

"Do I need to dare you?"

I made myself smile.

"Why won't you?"

Vincent came towards us; as he approached, Angela pulled away from me. He studied her, and as he studied her she rubbed the back of a hand. With a quiet voice, Vincent said, "Nigger." I saw Angela's fingers spread, and she stepped towards Vincent, who raised an arm. She said "I'll kill you." He lowered his arm, and Angela lowered her hands.

"I'm sorry I said that," she said to Vincent.

Vincent touched his throat.

In street clothes, Carole came to the bar and put her purse on it. She opened the purse and from it took a bottle of fingernail polish and she began to paint the nails of a hand.

"What happened?" Angela asked her.

"I got the money," Carole said.

"What did you have to do?"

"Never mind."

"Do you want a drink, honey?"

"No, I'm all right."

"Do you want me to do your other hand?" Angela asked.

"Thanks. I wouldn't mind."

Holding each limp finger in turn, Angela painted Carole's large nails.

For some reason, I turned to Vincent. Angela, her eyes shifting, caught me looking at him. She said to me:

"So what are you gawking at?"

"Me?" I asked, pointing to myself.

"All you do is sit back and gawk at us. Why don't you go away? What do you want, gawking at us? What? What are you here for?"

I kept my hand, my index finger out, at my chest.

"All right. I know. If you want to see something different," Angela said harshly, "I'll show you something that'll really change your life." She stepped away from the bar. "We're going out."

"Who?" Carole asked.

"Whoever wants to come."

"Where're you going?"

"You'll find out." But she didn't move. She said, "Everybody wants something from me—" She put her hands on the edge of the table.

Slowly, Vincent said, "Let's go."

"Go?" Angela said.

"Come on."

Angela said to him, "Vincent, you're a good man, I know—"

Vincent put a finger to the middle of his forehead and pressed it, his eyes closed.

"All right," she said, "all right."

6

IN the crowded taxi, no one spoke because Vincent didn't speak. The driver took us fast through the empty streets, past the terminal of the trolley line, and past empty lots beyond which I saw dark mountains. On a street, one house, behind a garden wall, was lit up. The street was not paved and was rutted. The taxi parked by the garden wall. Angela told the driver to wait. Vincent was the last to get out. I stayed close to Angela as she went ahead of Carole to the gate.

By the door at the back of a large room, lit by floor lamps, a man on a wooden chair tuned a guitar. There were few people at the tables in the room.

Vincent led us to a table.

The table next to us was empty, but at the one beyond was a circle of five young women and one young man. The man was silent, the women talking and laughing, their bodies moving as though they were half dancing. Their black shining hair was held up from their white napes by combs; they touched one another, on the arms, the shoulders, the breasts, and one woman put her hand about the nape of the one nearest to draw her close and kiss her. The young women were beautiful; the young man, in a white suit, was beautiful too. Angela tapped her nails on the table about which our silent group sat.

After a while, the young women and the young man got up and left the room by the doorway next to the wooden chair on which the guitarist had left his guitar.

An elderly woman with white hair came over and whispered to Angela, then she left.

Angela said, "She asked us if we want to go upstairs now."

"Count me out," Carole said.

Angela's eyes were almost closed.

With a little jerk of my body, I thought: it was ridiculous, it was childish to think that, behind the walls about me, people were doing what it was impossible for me to imagine.

"Do you know what happens up there?" Angela asked in a soft voice.

"No." One of my elbows jerked, and a knee, as if it had been sharply hit.

She said to me, her lips slightly parted, "So?"

Carole said, "Well, if someone pays for me."

Vincent smiled. His smile puckered his lips. "I'll pay for you," he said.

"I'll come," Carole said. "I'll come up." She looked up at the ceiling.

When Vincent turned to me, I felt a little shock, which I had been expecting.

"What about you? I'll pay for you, too."

I said, "Are you testing me?"

Angela said, "Yes."

"That's it," Vincent said, "dare him, and see what he'll do."

"I dare you," she said.

I stood. My knee caps loosened and trembled.

"Come on," I said.

Blinking, Carole said to me, "Quit joking. We've all just been joking. Let's cut it out."

"No, no. Come on."

"You really want to go up there?" Carole asked.

"Yes, I do."

My pulse beat so I imagined I might suddenly lose control of my body. "Are you coming?" I asked. "Aren't you?" I asked Angela.

Angela rose. She remained before her chair. What, after all, is promised? I thought. As slowly as she had stood, Angela sat. I sat, too.

Angela opened her purse, searched in it, and put out on the table small centimos coins and dirty frayed bills which she found at the bottom.

"We're going home," she said. "No one's going upstairs. How much money do we have?"

Carole took out a small money purse. "Not much."

Vincent said nothing.

"I'll pay," I said. "I want to pay for everything."

"No," Angela said, "nothing from you."

She counted out money from her purse, and took the frayed bills Carole gave her.

When we stood, the guitarist came into the room. Angela said something to him in Spanish and led us out quickly.

Walking, I thought my ankles, knees, thighs, backbone, arm joints were dislocated, and I would fall apart. In the taxi, I pressed against the seat back. When I yawned I shook more. The shaking lessened as the taxi sped through the streets. It stopped at the train station.

Vincent remained in the taxi, and Angela leaned in, talking to him quietly. I thought she was saying good-bye to him. I went near Angela to get a closer look at him in the taxi. With a slight panic, I thought: he can't be going away. Angela was not saying good-bye. She was saying, softly, "Please get out. Please get out of the taxi." I moved away, towards the station entrance, where Carole was standing.

Carole said, "He wants her to go with him, does he?"

"I don't know."

"She'd better not go with him."

"What would he do to her?"

Carole raised her eyebrows. She knew she'd better not get involved.

"He wants her to go with him," she said. "She should've known that once she came back to him he wouldn't ever let her go again. She shouldn't have come back. She was crazy."

"Why did she leave?" I asked.

"He was going to kill her."

I laughed, suddenly.

"Don't laugh," Carole said.

I stopped laughing, and frowned when I saw Vincent get out of the taxi; while Angela paid the driver, he stood beside her, then she took his arm and they came towards the station entrance.

Carole said, with a hard voice, "So she's got him to come with us."

I kept a distance as we went into the station, where poor travelers, wrapped in newspapers or old coats, lay asleep on the marble floor, in which the hanging overhead lights were reflected. The four of us walked among the bodies to the one open ticket window.

On the platform, Carole sat bent over on a wooden crate, her arms about her raised knees. I stood near her, but didn't talk to her, and after a while went to the edge of the cement platform, folded over the lapels of my jacket and put my hands in my trouser pockets. I kept glancing at Angela and Vincent as if I shouldn't.

The train came in and we got into a third-class compartment with wooden slat seats; the train lurched and we slid from side to side. I sat next to Carole. Across were Angela and Vincent. It was cold and there was a smell of coal smoke. Carole alone was speaking, quietly, to me. Her head, resting on the back of the wooden seat, wobbled.

She said, "I wasn't a very great success in cabaret in London, I admit, but other girls, much worse than I, had rich boyfriends, married well, had good lives."

"I'm sorry," I said.

"I wonder and wonder what's wrong with me. I don't know why I shouldn't have a better life."

Smoking, Angela threw the cigarette on the floor. "Cut it out, Carole." she said, her face screwed up against the smoke. "We've all been there. We know it. Cut it."

Carole said, "I was only saying—"

Her face more screwed up and her voice, too, twisted, Angela said sideways through teeth that I had not realized before were crooked, "I said cut it. Just cut out griping about what we've all had to go through."

Carole got up and stood before the dark window. She pulled the window down, and, on a blast of cold air, coal smoke blew into the compartment. Coughing, Carole shut the window. When she sat, she turned her head away from me.

Vincent looked out the window.

7

ANGELA led Vincent, Carole and me swiftly through the deserted streets. At a corner she stopped, not sure which way she should go; she pointed the way down a street with a black hand.

In the apartment, faint light came from the white walls, from the faces and hands of Carole and Vincent. Angela moved around, invisible, until she turned on a lamp.

Vincent took off his jacket and threw it down; he undid his tie, yanked it off, and threw that down. He removed his shoes and socks. Then he unbuttoned his shirt all the way down the front and at the cuffs and pulled the tails out of his trousers, and he held it away from his body as if to take it off, but, looking at Angela, he let it fall loosely about him. Angela put on another light. Vincent went out onto the balcony. As though drawn, Angela followed him out, and I, drawn too, followed. Carole remained inside.

Under the balcony was a narrow street which went down-hill to where palm trees along the seafront were illuminated by street lamps. Vincent leaned over the balcony, facing the sea. Side by side, Angela and I leaned against the wall.

"I shouldn't have been cruel to Carole on the train," she said.

Vincent turned away from the balcony edge and rubbed his bare arms and chest under his shirt.

From the apartment Carole came out onto the balcony, combing her hair with her fingers. She said, hollowly, "I've got a terrible day facing me. I should be in Barcelona preparing for it."

"We should all go to sleep," Angela said.

"I'll try to sleep," Carole said, and she went inside again.

Vincent let his shirt fall off. His arms and chest shone in the outside darkness. Touching his bare flesh, he came towards Angela and me. He was not just touching himself; he was pinching the flesh on his arms and chest and twisting it. He winced a little. When he reached out, I moved away. Angela pressed against the wall. I thought he would grab her skin at the side of her neck and twist it, but he touched her there with one finger.

"We've got to go to bed," he said.

"Yes."

"Let's go in," he said.

He let her pass before him. He picked up his shirt from the tiles and put it on as I followed after him.

Carole was slumped on the sofa. Angela roused her, and while she sat, slumped, in an armchair, Angela tucked sheets about the sofa cushions, spread a blanket, arranged a pillow. Vincent and I were at opposite ends of the sofa. Angela said softly to Carole, "Come on now," and Carole took off her dress, shoes, stockings, garter belt, and got under the covers Angela held up for her. When Angela, bent over, looked up at me, I could not bear the look, and left the living room to wander about the apartment.

123

The kitchen smelled of escaping gas. I opened a window. I walked more and more rapidly around the kitchen, as if I might walk suddenly out past a wall. I went into the passageway; and at the end of the passageway I saw Angela holding open the door to her room for Vincent to go in. I stepped back. Angela closed the door behind her.

I went quickly to my room, took off my shoes and socks, my trousers and underpants, and lay on my unmade bed. I lay still as the dawn light drew out in long fine lines through the shutters and formed the long perspectives of a space askew in the space of the room. After a while, I got up and stood in the strange space formed by the lines of light.

I ran my hands over my body, forehead, cheeks, jaw, nape, throat, shoulders, upper arms, under arms, chest, abdomen, thighs, buttocks, groin, cock and balls, inside my legs, my knees, calves. I did not touch my erection. I pinched my arms and thighs. Suddenly, a spurt of sperm fell to the floor.

I heard dogs barking outside, and peoples' voices, and the sound of wooden cart wheels on the cobbles. I could not tell what was going on in my head, in my body. That I couldn't tell made me want to vomit. I tried to concentrate on the distant sounds. But the more I concentrated on them the more they seemed to come from inside me. I shook my head, and shook my body.

What were they doing, now, in the bedroom on the other side of the wall from me?

Stop it, I said to myself, stop this.

Pack now and go before anyone is up. You will go with yourself and your money intact. Nothing will happen to you if you go now.

This thinking, as if it were the voice of someone else more intelligent than I, did calm me. I pulled the top sheet off the bed and wrapped it about my body, then went to my suitcase, open in a corner of the room, and knelt over it to put into it some dirty underwear and socks I'd thrown on the floor. But as I was packing away the dirty clothes, I took out, from among other dirty underwear and socks, the envelope containing my money, opened it, and ran my finger over the edges of the dollar bills and checks. I held the envelope for a time, then put it back into the suitcase, among the dirty clothes, next to the letter Madame Alberti had given me. I took other clothes out and got dressed. I packed and shut my suitcase.

Leaving the case in the corner, I left my room quietly and went along the passageway. The door to Angela and Vincent's room was shut. I leaned against a wall.

I thought: supposing he has killed her?

I walked down the passageway into the living room. It was filled with crude light. On the sofa, all that was visible of Carole was her disheveled hair, dry blond, dark at the roots. In an armchair, her back to me, was Angela. She had a large towel tucked about her. She turned when I stopped at the door.

I went back to my room, opened my suitcase and searched with my fingers under the dirty clothes for the envelope, then returned to the living room and went to Angela holding the envelope out.

She said, in a little girl's voice, "What's that?"

"It's the money."

"Oh."

"Take it."

With a limp hand, Angela reached out for the envelope and held it with her middle and index fingers; she let her hand and the envelope fall into her lap.

I said, "I have to sign over the traveler's checks."

She shook her head. I remained where I was. She put her hands to her breasts to hold the towel in place as she got up, and she stood before me.

Softly, she asked, "What are you going to do now?"

"I don't know."

Shrugging a shoulder, Angela looked at the envelope. She said, "If I were taking risks to change the world as it is into another world, at least some people would think my life wasn't a waste, as it is now."

My voice sounded near and far. "You think the world can't be changed?"

"No, honey, it can't be," she said. "You think it can?"

"Yes."

Angela grabbed me. I felt her hands on my shoulders, my back, the round side of my chest. She drew back a little from me, and I saw Angela become large, very near me, and, too, minute, very far from me—or perhaps the minute Angela was close to me, and the large Angela went further and further back, and the further back she went the larger she became. I raised my arms out from my sides and leaned a little forward, and she waited; I placed my hands on her shoulders, but I couldn't make myself hold her. My hands slid off her shoulders and my arms fell. She went down the passage into the room where, I supposed, Vincent was asleep.

8

SILENT, we walked up through the town in high sunlight. Vincent went first, then Angela, and, side by side, Carole and myself.

In the square outside the station we all stood together.

Carole said, "I don't think I have enough money for a ticket."

"I'll pay for it," Vincent said.

He gave her the money and she left us; to get into the station she had to go behind a large wooden ox cart, its shafts sticking up into the sky.

Angela was between Vincent and me as we continued along a street that became a path out of town. On the other side of the train tracks was a dirt road that ran along the tracks, and between the road and the tracks were agaves covered with red dust. The road diverged into a field. The earth was dry. We walked along the road to where it ended in a bank of stones and we climbed over the stones into another, higher field. Beyond this field was the arid mountain rising from terraces. Pouting a little, Angela looked at the mountain. Her hair, curling about her face, gleamed. The three of us walked through the field; we drew apart to pass rocks and cactus plants. From time to time Angela stopped to shake stone chips from her sandals. Red dust rose about us.

I opened my mouth to speak, but didn't.

Angela said, "What?"

"Nothing."

"I thought you were going to say something."

Vincent glanced at me. Then he turned away and began to hurry, and Angela and I hurried after him, over a wall of porous stones into a vineyard. The vines, supported by short sticks, were close to the ground and had large dusty leaves, and beneath the leaves were, in heavy bunches, the grapes. We hurried between the rows of vines. The great bunches of grapes pulled down the shoots that grew from the gnarled stumps; the grapes were sunlit. I had no idea why we were hurrying.

Angela stopped. Bending from the waist, she reached among vine leaves and broke a bunch away. She stood and held it up. "Vincent," she called. Ahead of her, he stopped and turned. The bunch gleamed. "What do you think of that?" she asked. Vincent shaded his eyes with his hands, and he came towards her. He nodded. She threw the bunch towards him; it hit him in the chest and he caught it in his arms. He nodded again, and smiled. "Yes," he said, "but you shouldn't pick those grapes, they're not yours." She laughed. "Hey," he said. She bent again to break another bunch away, which she flung into his arms. He clutched them, crushing some as he tried to keep the bunches from falling apart and dropping to the ground. "Listen," he said, "I—" But, even as he started to talk, she had another bunch, larger than the others; she held it by the stem with her clinched fist and she threw it at him. His arms were filled with bunches of grapes. He opened his arms and let the grapes drop to the ground.

He laughed. I had never seen him laugh. He said, "Beat me to the top."

Angela followed Vincent down a sloping field which then rose, in terraces, into the base of the mountain. I followed Angela. From time to time, she looked back at me, though, panting, she was walking quickly to keep up with Vincent. She stumbled, and I rushed ahead to her, but she rushed on ahead of me. The mountain appeared to be beyond the sunlight, dark. Vincent paused to help Angela up a dry stone wall, which, when I reached it, I saw was imbedded with seashells. We crossed a rocky terrace; among the rocks were cactus plants. We climbed to another terrace, planted with vines, and each of us went between a different alley. The grapes were clear, so the sun shone through them. I picked one and crushed it in my fingers and the pulp and seeds ran into my palm with the juice. Vincent, Angela always hurrying behind him, was on the next terrace. I, too, hurried to catch up, but I stayed behind them, hurrying in bursts.

At the next terrace wall, high, I reached Angela. She was trying to climb by wedging her toes between the stones and grabbing grass, but she kept falling back. I climbed and held my hand down to her to pull her up to the higher grading, where she went on after Vincent, half way across the steep, rocky terrace, and I hung back for a moment.

It was as if she were going after him not to beat him, but because she was alarmed at what he might do on the mountain.

Vincent reached another terrace wall, the last, and climbed it. He stopped when Angela called him, and he helped her up. He kept her hand in his, and with his free one brushed her tangled, gleaming hair from her face. Then he let her go and continued, ahead of her. I caught up with her as she was leaning against a big stone. Together, we watched Vincent climb towards some pine trees.

I said, "What's he doing?"

Her eyes large, she said, "You won't leave me, will you?"

I said, "I can't leave."

She didn't seem to understand. "Please don't leave me with him."

I shook my head a little.

Vincent was among the pine trees, running up the steep slope.

Angela said, "Help me with him."

"How?"

"I don't know. I don't know, myself, how." As she turned away from me to follow him, she turned back. "Maybe you should go."

"I can't," I said.

She went on, slipping on the rocks so she had to hold her arms out to keep her balance. He had disappeared among the pine trees.

I hurried along with Angela. "This is ridiculous," I said.

"I know."

As we climbed the rocky, rutted slope of the mountain, we clutched onto the branches of low dry bushes for footing.

"Doesn't he know it's ridiculous?" I asked.

"He sure does." As if to correct herself for being so idiomatic, she added, "Of course he does."

We were sweating as we went through the pine trees.

Further up, out of the trees, the sun glared on the smooth rock. We were walking now, heavily, and breathing heavily.

130

Just when I thought we'd reached the summit, a bulge of stone, I would see beyond it to another bulge. There was a breeze. Vincent was not visible anywhere. As we climbed over a bulge, I saw him. Angela stopped for a moment, frowning, as if to study him before she went on. He turned to her as she approached him and he smiled, a large smile. He was standing at the top of the mountain.

I heard her say, "Bravo." She was smiling.

From the mountain, the sky and the sea were flat and black, and the high sun was white. Because of the glare, I had to look away, to the coast on either side, where mountains sloped into the black sea.

A little thrill of joy passed through me when, looking back at Vincent, I saw him put his arms around Angela.

9

WE spent a week in the town by the sea.

For the first days, Vincent was quiet. I wondered
what he might do that was criminal. There was no talk of
jobs, but no doubt the jobs wouldn't have been talked about
in front of me. I'd have sensed the anticipation in Angela
if a job was being planned, and I didn't. I sensed only her
anxiety that he wouldn't remain quiet, that his quiet came
from some kind of exhaustion. Sometimes, at night, I woke
to a light from the living room shining around my door,
and I imagined it was Vincent who couldn't sleep, because
Angela, when we were alone, had slept ten hours a night,
often more. After a while, I would hear Angela call him
from their room, and he'd shut off the light, perhaps to return to her, perhaps to stay in the dark.

Each morning, he went out for an hour, and came back
with a newspaper, sometimes two, which he read on the
balcony in the sunlight.

Angela said to him, "Why do you want to read those
newspapers? You hate them."

Angela, I knew, did not want anything to happen. One

afternoon, we sat at the dining room table, each of us having cleared a space in the mess of stockings and magazines and dishes left from the last meal, to draw on sheets of paper with colored crayons. This was Angela's idea. And though I knew Angela always wanted to be doing something, in this case I thought she wanted us to be drawing to keep anything else from happening. We drank rough red wine as we drew.

It surprised me that Vincent, hunched over his paper was so intent on his drawing, a view from a window. He held it up by the corners for Angela and me to see it. I turned my drawing over. No one asked to see it.

Out to shop, Angela and I were down in the street, in shade under the balcony, waiting for a donkey, led by an old man, to pass. The donkey stopped in front of us and shat. I heard laughter above us. Angela and I looked up to where Vincent was leaning over the parapet. Vincent's chest was naked.

"You laughing at me?" she asked. "You take it back." Her face was hard and her eyes were large, so the irises bulged. "Take it back."

"No," he said.

I was alarmed because I had no idea where an argument between them would lead. I wanted her to give in to him, and wondered if I could make her by, somehow, giving in to him myself. And then she laughed.

Later, the three of us were in the living room, Vincent in an armchair, Angela and I on the sofa. It was hot, and we were sweating in the still air. Angela's neck was shiny with sweat, and the thin cloth of her bodice stuck to her breasts. She was talking, in a quiet voice, as if that was all she could do, she who always wanted to do something. I didn't know if it was because of Vincent, who seemed to be listening closely, but she talked about herself.

With a loose drawl, but carefully, she said, "I know I'm not very intelligent. I know I don't understand much about what's going on in the world outside, don't understand much of what's going on in this country. I think I'm not capable of understanding anything, really. Sometimes I pretend that I understand. I pick up a bit of information from what I hear someone say, or from glancing at a newspaper, and if I'm talking to someone I drop the bit—"

Vincent said, "You know more than you think."

Angela put her head against the sofa back.

I wondered if Angela thought that Vincent, though he said nothing to show he did, knew everything she and I didn't know, and knew it from experience in everything. But whereas she asked him, as if she had to, what we should have to eat for supper, I wanted to ask him other questions.

Angela said she would go out, alone, to do the shopping. Vincent said, "No, I'll go too." She said, "Stay here. It's too hot." I said, "I'll come, too." She said, "You stay here with Vincent."

We sat at the dining room table, drinking iced water. The skin of his shoulders and chest was moist. I would never have taken off my shirt in front of him, to expose even my chest.

After a long silence, I asked him, "How long have you been in Spain?"

He frowned. "Why do you want to know?"

"I guess I want to know how long people can stay abroad without wanting to go back."

He said, "I've been here about twenty-five years."

He wouldn't, I was sure, tell me any more, or I couldn't and maybe wouldn't ask him any more.

But when I thought about his living abroad for more years than I'd been alive, I realized he had been in Spain during the Civil War.

He must have known I had realized this when, at some moment after, I said, "It has to change people, going through a war."

"What do you mean?"

"Well—"

"Come on. Tell me what you mean."

"I mean that after, everything must seem—"

"What?"

I knew that anything I said would be wrong. I had never been through war. As a sweat oozed out over me, I crossed my arms and said, "It must make you feel you can't say anything about it, not even that—"

"What? What? Come on."

I uncrossed my arms. My body was wet beneath my clothes. "Somehow, I don't know how, but somehow I think that, in a war, you probably think, this isn't the way I imagined it'd be, this isn't really serious."

"And that's how you imagine war changes people?"

"They see that what should be serious, because the suffering is so terrible, so much greater than any suffering that they'd known, isn't real—" I stopped.

"And what do you think is?" he asked.

I said, "Well, I've never suffered."

When I looked at him, I saw he had put his hand over his forehead and partly covered his eyes; but he still looked at me from under his hand.

He said, "People suffer."

As with the pang of a small plea, "Tell me about the war," I asked.

"No," he said.

I felt weak. I went to my room and lay on my bed.

But maybe he continued to think of what I had asked, because, after supper while we were sitting at the messy table, he said that he wasn't crazy, that something else was wrong with him but he was not crazy. He knew very well that the war was still going on in Spain, but there was no reason why he should think about it. It was not his war, had never been, as this country was not his country, and never was. What the hell was he thinking about? He hit his head. "I've got to stop thinking like this. I don't want to think like this. Angela, stop me from thinking like this."

"Let's play cards," she said. "We'll play for money. You like playing cards for money."

He put his hand to his forehead. "All right."

There was, I noted, something odd about the way he spoke, as if he had not grown up with the language, but learned it, and all the while he spoke he had to think about it. He frowned a little when he spoke, slowly, with the "g" sound hard. Listening to him, I thought that he had really become a foreigner, that he no longer had anything to do with what I knew as an American. I listened with attention, frightened by his foreignness.

The fourth morning, Angela and I went out with Vincent to a café in the main square for breakfast of coffee and rolls. While Vincent read a Spanish newspaper, Angela and I watched people walk across the square. Often, when one spotted Angela, the man or woman stopped to stare at her blackness, and Angela smiled.

Vincent folded his newspaper and slapped the edge of the table with it. A knife fell from a plate.

A little shock passed through Angela.

"They think they can tell you what to do," Vincent said.

Quickly, Angela said, "Look, Vincent, look at that little girl in her first communion dress."

I realized it was Sunday morning. I had not been to church since my first Sunday in Paris.

"They think everybody's in the army," Vincent said. "They think they have absolute rights over you." He picked up the newspaper and hit the table with it.

"Vincent, stop it," Angela said.

She nodded towards a corner of the small square, where two civil guards had appeared from a side street. Their rifles were slung over their shoulders, and they walked side by side towards the café. They passed. They were ten steps away from us and Vincent spat on the cobbles. A great thrill passed through me when one of the civil guards turned to look, first at the cobble where Vincent had spat, then at Vincent, whose face was tense as he returned the look, and I thought: this is it. Angela was holding the edge of the table. But, his facial muscles sagging, Vincent lowered his eyes. He hunched his shoulders and put his hands, folded together, between his knees. The civil guards walked on. I felt my own body sag.

Vincent said. "How I hate this country."

As from a distance, I asked, "Why don't you go away?"

"Where?" he asked me.

"Back to America," I said.

"I haven't had a passport for almost as long as I've been here."

"What did you do with it?"

"I gave it to someone."

"And you've stayed here all these years without being asked for your passport?"

"No. I've been asked."

"And what do you do when you're asked?"

He stared at me, and as he stared one eye remained open and the other closed.

Angela said, "Come on, let's go home. We'll do something at home."

I had no money. Angela paid.

When we got to the apartment, searching as if for someone in it, Vincent said to Angela, "You left a glass of water on the table in front of the sofa."

That he picked out a glass of water from the confusion of other things made me wonder what was wrong with the glass of water.

Angela said, with a slight whine, "It doesn't matter."

It was I who had left the glass of water there, but I couldn't admit that I had. I seemed to become magnified around myself.

"That glass of water shouldn't be there. Go pick it up and put it in the kitchen."

Angela turned away.

He spoke from the side of his mouth, like a commanding sergeant: "Go take it away!"

I could see her, too, expand around herself, and I knew that she, like me, had to hold herself against that threatening magnified self, by being still, or trying to be.

He shouted, "Do it!"

Her fingertips to her temples, she remained still.

I expanded more, so I was distorted.

Lowering her hands, Angela turned back to him. She said, her voice low, "Vincent, it isn't important. It's an unimportant detail. You can't reduce everything to such details."

"It is important. Go take it away."

She appeared to be carrying a weight. Her voice went even lower. "Please, Vincent, I can't any more, I can't be made to think of every single little detail. Please don't make me."

"You've got to think of every detail."

She pressed the back of a limp hand to her forehead, and I saw tears come to her eyes. She shook her head. "What are you doing to me?"

His voice made her jolt. "Stop this!"

I, too, was jolted.

Tears were running from her eyes, and she smeared them across her cheeks. "I'm not faking," she said. "I'm not."

"You are."

"Please."

"Go pick up the glass of water."

She swung her body away from his towards the table, her hand reaching out, but she said, weeping, "What do you want to make of me?"

A kind of slime came out all over my body as I went past Angela to the table and picked up the glass of water. I walked to the kitchen and poured the water into the sink, rinsed the glass, dried it, and put it in a cupboard, and it seemed to me I was watched closely all the while. I stayed for a long while in the kitchen, taking the dirty dishes from the table and counters and washing them and putting them away. Sometimes I wanted to throw the dishes against a wall, or the floor, to smash them.

When I came out into the living room, Angela was laughing. She was standing before Vincent, who was in an armchair, and she was laughing, one hand across her mouth, the other at her doubled-over waist, as at some wild joke. And Vincent was laughing too, or smiling. But they didn't tell me what the joke was, and I thought it might be about me.

My reactions, laughing or crying, did not, as my reactions, count; they were, because they were mine, not to be trusted. But some force in me, deeper than my deep passivity, would react. Not I, not I, false, would laugh or cry, but someone inside me would laugh or cry, and I would not be able to stop him, and I would laugh, too, or cry, most likely cry, because I felt such suffering, I felt in that someone who stood deep inside me, deeper than my falsity, great suffering.

I was in love with Vincent.

If I could, I would show him, with some small, elliptical gesture which implied a great, open gesture, that I loved him, but I couldn't, I couldn't make my gestures small, elliptical enough for him to take them seriously.

10

THE morning light woke me. I dressed slowly, then, barefoot, went along the passageway to the living room, but stopped at the door when I saw Vincent, naked, in the armchair; his legs were extended, an elbow was on the arm of the chair and his hand over his eyes, as if protecting them from the light in the room. The room had changed.

Or partly changed. The dining table was clear, and shone; the buffet was the same. There was not one object on them. The mirror that had hung over the buffet was gone. The chairs were placed squarely against the table. Two small rugs had been rolled up and pushed against a wall. On the floor was stacked a pile of magazines and by it was a heap of things: stockings, shoes, shower cap, envelopes and crumpled paper, a banderilla, knives and forks, a plate, a cup, an empty wine bottle, a necklace, a wine skin. Between the dining area and the sitting room area was a low wall, and all the glass bottles, dried flowers, seashells, melted candles, beach stones had been removed from it and placed on the floor. In the sitting area, attempts had been made to clear away, to make space, but it was as if here the effort required was too great, and the work was left; an orange crate filled with things stood among more things. It could only have been Vincent, alone, who had worked silently to do all this, and who had given it up in the end as too much. That he should have worked naked, his body bumping against the edges of furniture, seemed to me to make his work private, and I thought I should turn and leave him.

But he lowered his hand. I saw, before he saw me, a look in his eyes as of having hurt himself, bodily, and having had to sit, trying to still the pain. Then he saw me, but his expression didn't change; his pain appeared to me like his nakedness, which he made no attempt to hide. Both made me self-conscious, and self-consciously I smiled. I put a hand on the jamb of the door. He smiled a little, and raised his hand to his face again.

It was a fine smile, crooked at one corner, and it made his pain, physical or not physical, all at once false. He was not in any pain at all. It was as if Vincent knew what he was doing, was affecting pain—the pain, perhaps, of nothing but awareness of the things in the room, and, alone, he was seeing himself, alone, doing this. His smile had been a smile of embarrassment, as mine had been.

And it occurred to me: maybe he was simply embarrassed about being found naked.

He lowered his hand, and, his eyes still closed, swung his head from side to side, then let it hang loosely, his chin on his chest. I remained at the doorway. I was sure that it was because he didn't know if I was there or not that he raised his lids to glance in my direction; and, seeing me, he lowered his lids and I saw come over his face, come over his body, a flush. But he slouched lower in the chair and spread his legs out wider, so the hair in the crack between his buttocks showed, and he pressed both hands to the sides of his face.

As I turned away, Angela, on tiptoe, her body swaying in a swaying, loose robe, came towards me.

She whispered, "Is he there?"

"Yes," I said; attempting to make my voice normal, I knew I made it too loud.

She went into the living room and I followed her.

With quick movements, she began to collect objects together. She piled some onto the wide skirt of a dress spread out on the floor, then folded the shirt up and dragged the bundle across the floor, into the entry, and threw it into the empty maid's room. She moved silently. I saw a look of worry on her face. She was trying to lift the stack of magazines, and some slipped. I went to her.

I whispered, "I'll help."

Separately, and yet together, meeting at points about the areas, we collected all the objects and brought them to the maid's room, or put them away into the drawers of the buffet. The look of worry did not leave Angela's face; she was eager to clear the rooms before Vincent moved. That she was clearing them for him, because he couldn't bear them and had been unable himself to clear them, I saw; and I also saw, but not so openly, that she knew that if she did not clear them away he would do something bad. Sweating, I pulled the orange crate out of the room, past Vincent, followed by Angela with her arms filled with dangling clothes entwined with a black lace mantilla.

I tried to put a little order in the maid's room, and when I returned to the living area I saw Angela in the dining area, the other side of the separating wall, bending to collect bottles from the floor. All of Vincent's concentration was on her. There was this look in his eyes: of wonder, of bemused wonder. I stood back from them both. Angela had five bottles in her arms. She was involved in her work, as if, doing it, she could not think of anything but it. Vincent smiled and put a finger to his cheek. I thought: I don't understand you, not at all.

Angela went out. There was very little left in the room. On the low, wide table before the sofa was left only a tall green wine bottle, and I saw him stare at it and frown. It was as if as he stared at it it stood out a little from itself, and became incomprehensible, and the incomprehensibility made him wince. I went and grabbed the bottle by its neck and went into the dining area, put it in a drawer, and closed the drawer. I thought: but in a way I do understand. The smile he gave me, so slight and yet crooked, falsified his frown. It was a conspiratorial smile, as if he were saying: I see that you see what I'm up to. But then I wasn't sure, because as he looked towards the door through which Angela was entering, his frown suddenly struck me as an expression of a deep, if crazy, helplessness in him. Angela stopped, her mouth a little open.

She stopped because Vincent stood. He looked down at himself as though it just occurred to him that he was naked; he put his hands on his breasts. There was commiseration in her eyes, or fear; or perhaps there was both. She appeared to move a little towards him and, at the same time, to move away. As he went towards her, I noticed the scar on his body: the scar over a shoulder, diagonally across his chest. Then, with what longing, I thought, with what a strange longing did he go to her and put his arms around her and place his face against the side of her black neck? She held him to her. The skirt of her loose robe folded about his naked legs. They stood holding one another, and I watched them; he swung away from her and, an arm about her, took her down the passage to her bedroom.

I sat in the armchair he had occupied, in the light-shafted, spacious room.

An hour later, Angela came out of the room. She was dressed.

She said, "He's asleep."

We went out to a café on the sea front. We sat with glasses of beer.

Angela said, "I don't like the way he makes me think about myself all the time. I really don't."

"What does he make you think about yourself?"

"He makes me think I'm strange."

"And you don't think you are?"

"Oh, I want to be strange. I try to be. But, no, I'm not. You know I'm not. I'm not any stranger than you are, and you're not strange, not at all, though you want to be, too. Don't you see?"

"Yes."

"And I don't like the feeling he gives me of being strange."

"What is that?"

"Oh, really, really and truly strange."

"Not faking it?"

"No, not faking it."

I drank my beer and looked past the traffic along the road by the sea, and it seemed to me that I had been here, that years before I'd come abroad to be in such a place.

The café doors were open, and, just inside, a fat man was standing close to a thin man, and the fat man was counting out into the hands of the thin man a thick stack of peseta notes. Everyone was attentive to them. From time to time, the fat man licked his thumb. The counting took at least five minutes, and when it was finished the thin man, now holding the stack, seemed not to know what to do with the money, which was too much to put into his pocket, so he picked up a paper napkin from a table and wrapped the money in it. Holding his package, he invited the fat man to the bar for a drink. People outside kept watching them through the glass front of the café.

Angela said, "That looked like a lot of money."

After drinking his glass down in one go, the thin man came out of the café and walked past us, carrying his package. He took a side street up into the town.

"We'd better get back," Angela said.

In the apartment, she went into her bedroom and closed the door. For a long while, I wandered about the apartment. Then, out on the balcony, I quickly slipped off my clothes and lay on them on the tiles. The smell of my body in the sunlight made me get up, dress, and go into the living room. I lay on the sofa and fell asleep, and woke when the sun was low. Angela's bedroom door was still closed.

I could no longer stay in the apartment, and went out. I walked down by the beach, and out onto a stone breakwater into the sea. The sun behind me, the sea was white. As I was walking back towards the beach, I saw, on the sand below, partly screened by a boat on its side, a man and a woman lying side by side. They were wearing narrow bathing suits. They were touching one another. They must have known that anyone passing along the breakwater would see them, but if they glanced up and saw me, that only made them laugh and draw closer to one another as their hands stroked one another's arms, shoulders, breasts, thighs. I went on, slowly.

Because I didn't have my key on me, I had to ring the buzzer. I waited, and no one replied over the intercom. I buzzed again, and, again, no one replied. Maybe they had gone out, I thought, and a sense of dislocating panic came over me. I tried the buzzer again. About to go away to find them, I heard Angela's hoarse voice ask, "What do you want?" I said, "Let me in." There was a pause during which I thought she wouldn't let me in, and then I heard the clicks and opened the door. Upstairs, the door to the apartment was open. The door to the bedroom, however, was shut. In the kitchen, I looked for something to eat, and took to my room a piece of stale bread and two overripe tomatoes.

11

During the night, I woke to voices. I listened. They came from the living room. Mostly, it was one voice, Vincent's, and only occasionally Angela's. I couldn't make out what he was saying, but no doubt he couldn't sleep, and he kept Angela from sleeping, talking. His voice was low, level. I heard him say, "No, that's not it," in a voice louder than hers, then I heard her say something I didn't understand in a lower voice than his, and I imagined that while he sat she walked about. Then his voice too retreated and advanced; it was because I was falling asleep and waking, falling asleep and waking. I fell asleep.

There was silence when I woke again in the morning, but I found Angela and Vincent still in the living room, she stretched out on the sofa, and he, naked again, in his chair.

Vincent was examining his chest, probing at it with his fingers and raising the flesh into welts to examine it more closely. He raised his arms and smelled his armpits. Then he went back to studying his chest.

Angela lifted her head and said to me, "Come in." She lowered her head.

I came in and sat on the second chair, without arms. Then, as if with a shock, Vincent put his hands over his forehead. Angela stood, to step towards him. She stepped back, her arm up to protect herself, when he suddenly stood. He seemed to take a jump. "We'll go out," he said. "We'll do something. Come on. We'll all go out and do something. All right? Is that all right?"

She said, "You'll have to put on some clothes to go out."

As he passed the glass doors onto the balcony, he paused to glance at his reflection, and, as he stepped away, he swung his buttocks towards the reflection as if to see them, and he put a hand on one before he left.

Angela asked me, "What will we do? Can you think of anything to do?"

I wondered if she, who was very tired, was making it my responsibility.

We went to the beach below the high, square, brown church, where there were two old women and children playing in the surf. We lay on the white sand.

Pressing my head into the sand and arching my neck back, I saw, above my head, the church on the rocks, and I thought it was odd that when you sighted something you knew from a different angle it stood out in unexpected dimensions and it was as if you were seeing it for the first time. When I sat up and looked round at the church, it appeared to me as it always did, and went flat, and I no longer saw it. I lay back again, stared up, my eyeballs turned up in their sockets. They began to tear and I closed my eyes.

Vincent was next to me on the sand, and Angela was next to him.

I heard the surf and the cries of the children; they sounded much further than they were.

When Angela said, "It's hot," that sounded much nearer than she was.

But when I opened my eyes, Angela and Vincent had gone. The sand where they'd lain was dented, and there were trails of smaller dents towards the sea. In the glare I could hardly see past the two old women in bulging bathing suits sitting in the surf, while about them five naked children ran and splashed. I stood.

A figure was swimming in the glare towards the shore, and another figure was behind. They both appeared black. Then Angela rose up, and walked, stumbling a little, but before she reached the surf she turned back. Vincent rose out of the light. On the beach, he stopped; he breathed in deeply, so his shoulders rose, his chest expanded, his stomach was drawn in. He swung his head so water sprayed from his hair, and he walked up the beach. It seemed to me the world was attentive to him, and he was not in any way attentive to the world; all he was attentive to was a fly which buzzed about his wet hair and which he tried to brush away with a small gesture.

Angela followed him.

She and I continued to watch him do calisthenics in the sand; he fell forward, putting his hands out just in time to break his fall, and did pushups; then, with a jerk, he turned over, raised his legs high, until his weight was on his shoulders and nape, and he pedaled his legs high; then, with another jerk, he was standing and running in place. His narrow muscles stood out in his slim body; the welt of the scar showed white.

Jumping in place he made fists of his hands and jabbed at the air. His hair was in wet strands, shaking about. He turned towards Angela, and jabbed a fist towards her, and said "Come on, come on," and, hopping from one foot to the other, he jabbed at her lightly. She took a position, her arms folded in against herself, her hand closed into fists, and they sparred. When her fist grazed his shoulder, he fell back as from a blow, spat with his tongue extended, and came back for her, his head lowered into his shoulders. Angela laughed and took her position again; he didn't laugh, and his face was stern, but he might have been laughing. Angela moved quickly, deftly; he slowly and heavily. She blocked a blow, and he threw up his arms. "Come on you mother-fucker," Angela said, "come on." As they continued to spar, the sand rose in spurts about their feet. Angela's fist shot out, made contact with his jaw, and he, his arms and legs spread out, fell into the sand. He raised himself a little. His tongue out, spitting, he shook his head; his eyes were crossed. Then he collapsed backwards akimbo, and was motionless.

Angela's laughter dropped away, but she smiled when he suddenly jumped up and put an arm around her.

And yet, when he turned away and looked towards the sea wall, a fear appeared to come over her face as to what they should do next, as if it had to be up to her again to think of what they would do, as though he demanded it of her. She turned towards the sea wall.

I, too, must think of something to do, but I could think of nothing. Angela and I would exaggerate any happening. My attention already exaggerating in anticipation, I also turned.

Above the sea wall, on the road bordered with palms and green benches, were people grouped about the narrow entrance of a street between white houses, and from the street a black horse was emerging, its lowered head plumed with black feathers.

"What's that?" Angela repeated.

Vincent sat on the sand.

"What is it?" Angela said, her voice higher.

But Vincent simply lay and stretched his arms above his head and yawned. Sand adhered to his wet skin.

"We'll go see," Angela said to me.

We went past some fishing boats on the beach to the sea wall, but stopped below it. The horse pulled a hearse out onto the road; there were plumes at the corners of the hearse, and silver trim about the window at the side which showed a heap of crushed flowers. The hearse swung from side to side on its larged spoked wheels. Walking behind was a priest in a black and silver cope, followed by two altar boys, one carried a long gold crucifix and the other a censer. After came a woman in black, a veil over her head, and her hands under the veil; she was supported on either side by two women in black. A man with a black band on the upper arm of his suit jacket was behind; then came others, silent, their hands clasped. The procession passed the cafés. At the end was a straggling group of men and women gesturing and speaking quietly.

I turned to Angela. We went back.

His head to the side, Vincent's mouth was open and saliva ran from a corner. His lids fluttered.

"He's asleep," she said.

"He kept you awake all night?"

I looked round at the funeral procession; it was going up the dirt road to the cemetery behind the church. Because of the funeral, even the children on the beach were still.

Angela sat beside Vincent, a towel wrapped over her shoulders, and I took a walk along the beach and stood in the shade of a reed awning. From a distance, as I walked back, I saw Angela sitting as before by the body of Vincent; she had drawn the big white towel over her head, so it covered her completely but for her black face. Vincent's body shone white. I sat at the other side of him from Angela.

The sun was high. The old women were leaving with the children. In their absence, the beach as I faced outward to the sea appeared never to have had a human foot set on it. Distorting heat waves rose.

Vincent rolled over onto his stomach. His hair was matted with salt and sand. The side of his face was pressed into the sand, towards me, and his eyes were open. It occurred to me that he hadn't been sleeping, not for a long while, but simply lying there. He turned to face Angela.

Quietly, she said, "Shall we go home?"

"No," he said in a gravel voice. "I don't want to go home."

"You're getting too much sun. We'll go to the stand and sit in the shade and have some beer."

"I don't want to go," he said.

She seemed to be judging his tone of voice. She said, "Come on."

She got up, the towel over her head and hanging over her shoulders, held about her by her fingers delicately grasping the edges together under her chin. Vincent got up.

I felt that I was lost. I walked behind Vincent, examining the back of his neck, the white flesh under an arm, the hollow behind a knee.

Under the striped shade of the reed awning we sat on a bench, Vincent between Angela and me. The cement floor was covered with sand and the caps of beer and soda bottles. Vincent drank his beer as if he had just woken up, and could not concentrate on anything beyond the beer; he seemed to be unaware of the cement floor, the caps, the sand, the cinder-block stand, the awning, on which the thin reeds were tied together by string, and the sunlight glinting through. He seemed, now, to be, in his lack of awareness, unprotected; he might have been a young boy or an old man incapable of any concentration beyond what he was drinking, and even in that he held the bottle out and looked at it, uncertain of what he was doing. When he finished, he placed the bottle between his feet on the cement.

"Do you want another?" Angela said.

"No," he said. "No, thank you."

"We'll go home," Angela said.

He said, "I don't want to."

"I know," she said, "but we'll go home now."

He walked silently between us. At street turnings, he, disoriented, left us to go the wrong way, and Angela would say, "This way," and he, silent, came with us, sometimes bumping into us.

While I waited outside the shops with Vincent, Angela went in to buy food. I continued to examine him, and though he knew I did, it was as if he could do nothing to stop me. It was as if he had to accept my examination. I took the parcels from Angela when she came out. We kept Vincent between us.

Inside the apartment Angela took the towel from about herself and put it around Vincent. She said, "Go take a shower." He went into the bathroom.

Angela and I were in our bathing suits. We listened to Vincent in the bathroom, talking to himself.

Angela said, "Let's get some food prepared. Maybe he'll eat. If we can get him to do something, we'll be all right."

After I dressed, quickly, I joined her in the kitchen. She was wearing a long, full dress, and her hair was tied up tightly.

While I was setting the dining table, Vincent came in, naked. He was running his hands through his wet hair. He wandered around the table, and asked as if for a moment he had forgotten her, "Where's Angela?", but didn't wait for me to answer. He was leaving just as Angela came in carrying a platter with, on one side, slices of oiled bread with tomatoes crushed on them, and, on the other side finely cut raw ham.

She said to Vincent, "Sit down."

He sat.

She said to me, "Go get a bottle of cold white wine."

We both watched Vincent, naked, eat and drink.

Angela said to him, "Don't you think you should put on some clothes to eat?"

His eyes focused with a sudden sharpness. "Why?"

She tried to smile.

He continued to eat. Then, his mouth full of food, he said, "I don't wear clothes when I don't need to wear clothes." He ate more. He said, "The fact is, I'm not wearing clothes because if I wore the clothes I came in, they'd become unwearable. If there hadn't been an old bathing suit here, I wouldn't have been able to go to the beach. I've got to keep my clothes for when I need them. I won't go around wearing wrinkled, dirty clothes."

"You can borrow some clothes." Angela said to me, "You'd like to lend him some clothes, wouldn't you?"

I imagined him not only with my money but with the clothes I'd put aside—clean socks, underwear, shirts, a light-weight suit—for the moment when I, I had thought, needed them, though I'd never really imagined what the moment would be: it would simply be special.

I said, "Well, yes."

Vincent picked up his glass of wine. He looked at it for a while, and then he put it on the table without drinking.

Angela said to him, "Vincent."

He said to her, "Do you think I don't know what you're trying to do? Do you think I'm a little boy or an old man, that I don't know what you're doing? Well, give it up. Give it up. You won't do it."

Her eyes narrowed on him. Her nose, too, narrowed on him. "No," she said, "You're wrong. All I'm trying to do, since I have to be with you, since you won't give me a choice, is to keep you from doing anything bad to me. That's what I'm trying to do. I'm trying to help myself."

"I see," he said.

"Now," she said, "don't make one of your scenes. Don't. I don't want one, won't stand for one. What you want from me, I'm giving to you. You've got it, you've got all my attention. You've got it. It's not for your sake, it's for my sake. But you've got it. Don't make a scene."

Holding the edge of the table, he pushed back his chair, and as he did he pushed the table also; the plates rattled, and the bottle of wine fell over. No one righted it. The wine poured out onto the wood and dripped off. Vincent stood.

He said, "I won't make a scene. I'm against making

scenes. You should know that. I'm against drawing attention to myself. You know that. I don't make scenes." He took a step backwards. I could see the muscles jumping in his jaw.

Angela righted the bottle and placed a paper napkin over the spilled wine.

"Sit down," she said. "I'll go get another bottle. Sit down."

"No," he said, "I won't sit down."

"Sit down," she said.

"No," he said. "I won't make a scene, but I won't sit down."

"There you are, stark naked, standing in the middle of the room. If that isn't a scene to attract attention, I'd like to know what is."

Vincent sat. Angela asked me if I'd go get another bottle of wine. We drank the wine in silence.

12

THE afternoon was long and hot. With Angela, I watched Vincent. There was always a worried look on her face of not understanding what he was doing when she turned to Vincent, in his chair, himself worriedly attentive to the details of his body: moles, hairs, pimples.

Angela switched on a ceiling light.

She asked me if I would go out to the beanery to buy some cooked beans for supper. She gave me the money. I hurried. The beanery was crowded. I stood behind a man in a dark suit, who was sweating; about the upper sleeve of his jacket was a black band. With the beans in a crock, and the crock in a net bag, I hurried back to the apartment.

As I entered I heard a repeated grunting sound from the living room, the sound of a man having sex, and I stayed in the entrance hall wondering if I should go back out. And as I stood in the entry, hearing those grunts which became, sometimes, whines, whimpers, I wondered what had taken him so extraordinarily far beyond ordinary self-consciousness. And so far above or below me, what did his self-consciousness reflect of himself? And did he intend, with a kind of heroic will, to go higher, lower, even further beyond the strange levels at which his self-consciousness reflected him? He had gone very far, further than I could ever make myself go. I swung the door one way then the other, telling myself I should go out, telling myself I should stay. I heard high howls, and as I turned to go I saw Angela, in her long, loose dress, step into the doorway of the living room. It was as if she was looking to see if I'd returned. She made a gesture to me to come quickly. I put the net sack with the pot of beans on the floor.

On the floor before his chair, Vincent was on his knees. He was pulling his hair. Keening, he rocked back and forth, back and forth, and uttered, in grunts, "Ah, ah."

My first reaction was to laugh.

Angela said, "He's seen something."

I suppressed my laughter.

"What am I going to do?" she said.

He pulled at his hair; he pulled at the flesh of his face as to pull it off, so his cheeks, mouth, nose were distended into those of the face of a grotesque. With each back and forth movement he grunted, and the grunts were expelled through his nose, like snorts. His eyes, red, were wide, and fixed on something a short distance from him. When his keening accelerated, the snorted grunts, too, accelerated, and then became a high continuous whine. As though, for a moment, what he was staring at disappeared, he searched the room for it, and his eyes struck Angela. A look of pleading came over his face, making it a human face; and, still rocking on his knees, he said to her:

"Do something! Do something to help me!"

Angela raised her arms. She was too frightened to go to him. As she raised her arms high, she turned away; and then something happened to stop her and she turned back.

He said to me: "Do something! Do something."

As if she were pushed, she stumbled toward him. Near him, she caught herself up, and was stepping back when he reached out and grabbed her legs. She shook her body.

She shouted, "Let me go!"

Vincent held.

"Let me go!"

Vincent let her go only to stand; she tried to get away, but he lunged for her and held her. His chin drawn in, he watched her; all she could move were her shoulders and head. Her arms were locked over her breasts; she shook her hands, in fists, and shook, trying to twist it, her body. Vincent was rigid.

I was terrified. I wondered if I was capable of killing him.

She let her body go slack, and as she did he loosened his hold on her, but kept his arms about her. It was as if she suddenly became very tired and he had to help her up. She put her head on his shoulder.

He said, "You're not going to go away."

"No," she said, "I'm not." She lifted her head from his shoulder and, her lids half closed, said, "I'm tired."

"I know. I've made you tired."

"We'll go to sleep. We must get some sleep."

Without even Angela glancing at me, they left the room.

In the entry I picked up the net bag containing the pot of beans. At the kitchen table, I cleared a space, and carefully set out a plate and a fork and knife and a glass on the wood. I thought about what I was doing. With a big wooden spoon, I scooped the still warm beans onto the plate, and then I opened a bottle of cold white wine, and I sat at the table to eat in the light of the dim over-hanging bulb. The next day, I thought, I would clear the kitchen and put order in it.

Angela came in. She said, "I'm starving."

"Take my place," I said.

"No."

"I'll set you a place."

"No. Just give me a plate of beans. Is there a clean plate?"

I found a clean plate and put beans on it.

"Is he asleep?" I asked.

"Yes." She leaned against the edge of the messy table and ate her beans; she kept her glass in a space between a half loaf of old bread and a felt slipper. "Don't ever let him into the kitchen," she said. "He'll have us cleaning it up like we cleaned up the other rooms. But he won't come in. He knows it's a mess."

We heard, "Angela," from the other room.

She lowered her plate.

"Angela, Angela," Vincent called.

She raised her plate and ate the beans quickly, and drank down the glass of wine.

It sounded from the bedroom as if he were hitting the headboard with his fists, and then the wall.

He shouted, "Angela!"

She ran out.

I washed some of the dirty dishes, glasses, pans piled on the table; but I began to feel there was too much to do, and I wouldn't be able to do it all, so I stopped. I left unwashed dishes in the sink and went to my room and sat on the edge of my unmade bed.

What consciousness survives self-consciousness? I wondered. None?

I undressed and lay on the bed and ran my hands over my body.

The last morning, I was woken by a gunshot. As from a violent nightmare, I sat up when I woke, and I wasn't sure, for a moment, if the sound hadn't occurred in the dream. I remained sitting, listening. I had never heard an actual gunshot; I was not sure what it would in fact sound like. I didn't lie back, because I thought that if I did and closed my eyes the sound would occur again. I listened for voices, for movement. I heard a dog barking far away.

And then I heard singing. Angela was singing, and with the singing was the strumming of a guitar, low and even. The words were unintelligible. She finished the song. Far away, the dog barked again. Angela repeated the song.

It wasn't a gunshot I'd heard, I thought. I got up and dressed. My clothes were limp and soiled, but I did not want to use clean ones. I went out.

Her legs under her long loose robe, Angela, on the sofa, held a guitar on her knees, and she didn't stop singing when I entered the room. It was the third time she was singing the same song. It was in French. When her lips came together they adhered a little, and when she parted them the soft flesh pulled. As she sang out, her lips swelled. At an angle across the room from her Vincent sat wrapped in a sheet. His eyes were on Angela. On the low table between them was a gun. I leaned against a wall.

Angela finished the song, her hands lightly resting on the guitar. Hunched in his sheet, his hair sticking out and his face unshaven, he looked like a survivor of a disaster. He pulled the sheet more closely about his shoulders.

I could see in Angela's red eyes that they had spent another sleepless night. Her body slouched over the guitar,
she struck the strings, lightly, and a chord rose. She put her
hand to her forehead. I knew what she was thinking; she
was thinking, well, it doesn't matter. She dropped her head
and raised her head and said to Vincent:

"You sing a song."

His eyes were heavy; he seemed to find his body too heavy
to move.

She held out the guitar. "Come on," she said, "you sing."

His voice was hardly audible. "No," he said.

"Come on," she said, and held the guitar out.

"No," he said.

She lowered the guitar to her lap.

"I don't sing any more," he said.

"Come on," she said.

"I can't get up," he said.

Swiftly, she went round the low table and handed him
the guitar; as he took it, the sheet fell away from his bare
arms and shoulders. As with great effort, he leaned forward
to the edge of the chair, one knee down, one up, and he
held the guitar in position against his body. As he settled it,
I saw, suddenly, that his body became rigid in an awkward
position. The guitar held at an angle against him, he looked
down at the floor as if not to look at us.

Angela and I waited.

I wanted to say, "It doesn't matter if you don't play."

As with an act of will, he raised an arm and struck a
chord. The reverberation seemed to produce a sweat on his
forehead, neck, shoulders. His lips twisted into a sudden

smile, that crooked smile; then he frowned to get the smile off his face. After another rigid moment, he lifted the guitar and held it out to Angela.

"I can't," he said.

She went to him saying, "It doesn't matter."

Before she could take it, however, he withdrew the guitar from her extended hands and paused and again settled it against his body. He kept his head turned away, so he was looking out over the balcony if he was looking anywhere, and, exerting a will to do what he did not want to do, he struck a chord, and played. He kept his eyes, turned away, open. His mouth hardly moved as he sang.

His voice was quiet, slack. As he sang, I thought: he has dared himself. My heart was large in my narrow chest. To sing at all, it was as if he were risking everything. His voice was hardly modulated, and I thought it might fade away.

"Connais-tu le pays où fleurit l'oranger—"

And he abruptly stopped, letting his strumming hand fall. He was still looking out over the balcony, and it was as if he stopped because he saw something that stopped him. The guitar slipped off his knee. He let it fall away from him and, he got up, leaving his sheet, and he walked over to the open glass doors to the balcony.

Angela, standing behind the sofa, said, "Vincent."

He turned to her. His eyes were clear and focused. "Yes?"

She did not know what to say.

"Yes?" he repeated. A slight frown of annoyance appeared on his forehead.

She raised her hands. "Well, nothing."

"Then why did you call me?"

"I'm not sure why. I just did."

"You must have had a reason."

"No," she said, "no reason."

"None?"

"No," she said, "none."

Still frowning a little, he went to the table and picked up the gun and returned with it to the balcony windows. He held it out and up, pointing it towards the sky. One eye closed, he took aim, perhaps at a bird, though from where I stood I couldn't see. I waited for him to fire.

He lowered his arm, and went to his chair, where he wrapped the sheet about himself. He kept the gun in his lap.

Angela remained on the other side of the sofa.

"We could go to Barcelona," she said.

"I don't want to go to Barcelona," he said.

"We don't know what's been happening. Maybe something's been happening at the club," she said.

He held up the gun and aimed it at a wall.

She said, "They're probably wondering what's happened to us."

"Let them wonder." He swung the gun to aim at another wall, and his arm stopped short. He lowered the gun. "What's that doing there?"

"What?"

He pointed with the barrel. "That."

He was pointing to a wine bottle on the wall between the sitting and dining areas.

Angela rushed to take it away.

"Leave it," he said.

She quickly drew back. He took aim at it. Angela put her hands to her head and turned away, her body bent. I waited for him to fire. He lowered the gun. I felt empty. He sat, his eyes fixed. Angela turned round to him.

She said, "Vincent, listen to me." She approached him

sideways. "We've got to get out." She was trying to make her voice sound matter-of-fact, practical. "You know what happens if you don't go out and do something." She approached closer to his side, but was ready to jump away. "What we'll do is, we'll go out on a job. That's what we'll do. It'll get us out doing something in the world. Listen to me."

He raised the gun again and held the barrel to his head.

"Listen to me," she said, "you like it. You like being out on a job."

He seemed to be thinking, but perhaps not, of what she was saying; he smiled slightly.

"Oh, Vince, come on," Angela said.

Still smiling slightly, he looked at her. "All right," he said.

"Then put the gun down."

He put the gun down. "All right," he said. "We'll do a job. All right."

"Then let's get ready," she said. "We'll get dressed and go into Barcelona now and see what we can set up. Let's go get dressed."

"I don't have any clean socks and underpants," he said. "I can't put on dirty socks and underpants."

Angela said to me, "You'll give him some, won't you?"

Her eyes were pleading.

"Of course," I said. "I'll give him anything he wants."

As I was taking the clothes out of my suitcase, open on the floor of my room, I knew that, in fact, I wanted to give them to Vincent, as I knew I had wanted to give him my money, as I would have given him anything—not, I thought, for his sake, and not for Angela's either, but for my own, though I in no way understood this.

I stood outside Angela's bedroom door with the clothes.

The door was ajar. I called. Angela said, "Come in." I didn't want to go in. She repeated, "Come on in." I pushed the door open and saw her sitting up on the bed and Vincent lying chest down, his face in her robed lap; she had her hands on his head. The room appeared huge with order.

13

IN my shirt, the two top buttons open, Vincent appeared cool, as if he had made his body temperature go down. But he had withdrawn into his coolness.

The neon sign over the club entrance was off, and the only one inside was the brutal-looking coat-check woman. She grunted in response to what Angela asked, but when Vincent spoke to her she answered at rapid length.

He said to Angela, "We'll have to make some telephone calls."

"I know you don't want to," she said.

"It doesn't matter what I want," he said.

They went into an office at the back of the club. I walked about the stark tables. Sunlight was beaming down through the long barred windows high up on one wall, and in the light the room did not appear to be a club, but a cellar where military police interrogated men.

I couldn't sit still. I heard Vincent's voice, then Angela's. While Angela was talking, Vincent came out of the office, and he, too, wandered about the tables. As I passed him I smiled. He stopped a few steps beyond me.

"Do you want to get involved in this?" he said.

I turned. "In what?" I asked.

"You know."

"No," I said. "I don't know."

Angela came out of the office and toward us.

We sat about as the sun drew back and left a gray light, and the club no longer seemed the cellar of a big building but a room that had nothing to do with the building, nothing to do with the outside. When the club became dark, the coat-check woman put on a dim light.

I said, "I guess you get used to waiting around."

Vincent said, "You have to get used to it. It's like being a soldier."

Suddenly, I asked, "Were you a soldier?"

"No," he said flatly, "no, I was never a soldier. I came to look at the war."

The telephone rang. Vincent said to Angela, "You answer it," and she went to the office. She was wearing her business suit and her high-heeled shoes. Vincent appeared to be trying to listen to what Angela said, but then, I thought, perhaps he wasn't listening to anything.

Angela came out. "It's all right," she said.

Vincent tipped back on his chair.

"We can go," Angela said.

He didn't move.

"Come on," she said. "We can go."

He tipped forward so the front legs of the chair jarred him.

We got into another taxi.

Angela said to Vincent, "You're in charge, remember, not me."

"You can do well enough on your own."

"I can't. I can't do anything on my own, you know that. Don't tell me that. Either you take charge or we stop now."

"We can stop anytime you want."

We got out at a corner. Vincent and I walked together behind Angela through streets that smelled of drains and escaping gas to a big apartment building with iron grille doors.

In the foyer we took a caged elevator up through the stairwell. Angela rang the bell, then stood back so Vincent would be before her. A woman answered, keeping the door half shut and half hiding behind it; then she opened the door. Down a passage, Vincent knocked on a door, waited, knocked again, and a voice sounded from inside; he opened and went in, but when I, from outside, saw a man and a woman in bed, I stayed back. By the bed, Vincent talked to them. Angela stood silently beside him.

The woman, in a slip, indicated me with her chin.

"Come in," Vincent said to me.

The woman got out of bed and put on a dressing gown.

"Here," she said to me, "sit."

My arms close to my sides, I sat on a thin-legged chair. She, crossing her thick legs, took an armchair across from me, and while Vincent and the man in bed talked in Spanish and Angela remained silent, the woman spoke to me in English. Perhaps it was her job.

She asked, "Where are you from?"

"America."

"First time in Spain?"

"Yes."

"Now, is too hot in Spain."

"Not really."

"You like it when is hot?"

"Yes."

"Vincent doesn't like it. It makes him sweat." She laughed a little. "I know Vincent very much. Very much. Where you meet him?"

"In the club."

"Yes, the club. You know Hal?"

"I do."

"Nice man. I like Hal. You like?"

"Yes, I do."

"Nice." She made a face. "You know Angela very much?"

"Much," I said.

"She love Vincent. No?"

"Yes, very much."

"She came back because she love him very much."

"Yes."

"And Vincent, he love Angela. Lovely couple, they. No?"

"Yes," I said.

Behind her, on the bed, the man was scratching his hairy chest as Vincent talked to him. Angela yawned. The man asked the woman for something, and she, barefoot, went for a briefcase on the top of a bureau and brought it to him. She propped up pillows behind the man, who opened the briefcase on his knees. It was filled with tagged keys. He picked up a bunch of keys, checked its tag, and handed them to Vincent. They shook hands. Vincent called me over to introduce me, and I shook hands with the man; his shoulder, arm, and the back of his hands were covered with thick black hair.

As if clasping a glass, the man raised a curved hand to his mouth and said to me, "Beba?"

"I'm all right," I said.

"Be friendly," Vincent said, "have a cognac."

"Am I being unfriendly?" I asked him.

"You will be if you don't accept a drink. You should be be friendly."

"I'll have a cognac."

Angela helped the woman with the cognacs. Translating, Vincent kept up a conversation about soccer as we drank. The man told Vincent to tell me he'd take me to a soccer match. I said to Vincent to say to the man that I'd like very much to go. Angela stayed back.

I wondered with what powerful will Vincent was able to act.

As if he thought I'd suddenly be able to understand, the hairy man spoke to me at length in Spanish.

The woman laughed. "He say to you, if you help, he pay you, too. You look like good boy. He give you money if you help get packages through." She laughed again and passed her hand through her hair. "My man too lazy. He never get out of bed, never leave room. He make other do for him. Safe for him, dangerous for other. But he pay good. He pay good people who work for him."

I tried to laugh. Angela said, "Let's go. Let's get out of here."

The woman showed us out into the darkness.

"We'll take another taxi," Vincent said.

We walked for a long while before we found one. We sweated. The taxi bounced us on the spring seat.

Vincent said to me, "You don't want to know what's going on?"

"No."

"You don't want to see?"

I didn't answer.

We went to Real Square. The club sign was lit, but we didn't go in; we sat at the café under the arcade on the corner.

We drank beers, which Vincent ordered. Whenever a man or a woman walked past the table, I looked a little anxiously at them; a man carried a basket, another wore a beret, a woman fanned herself.

I said finally to Angela, "Maybe I should go back to the apartment."

"Why?" she asked.

"I don't know. I—"

"Are you bored?"

"No, not bored. I—"

Vincent looked away, and we continued to sit. Around us, over what must have been hours, people sat, drank and smoked and ate shrimp from saucers, then got up and left and other people took their places at the metal tables. The beer went flat in my glass. When Angela asked me if I wanted more, I said, "No, thank you." "You haven't eaten anything." Vincent said. "I'm not hungry," I said. He ordered sandwiches and more beer. The waiter cleared the used glasses. I ate the sandwiches and drank the fresh beer. Tables were abandoned. The neon sign of the club, I noticed, went off, and there were many empty tables around us. The waiter came out to sweep up what had been thrown on the pavement.

Vincent yawned.

The waiter came out with his broom and said something to Vincent, and Vincent followed him inside. Through the plate glass window I saw him take a telephone receiver from the bar and speak. He hung up. He remained at the bar, where he ordered something to drink, and when he got the drink he put it beside the telephone and lifted the receiver and dialed, and I saw him speak again.

When he came out, his forehead, cheeks, jaw, neck were tense, and his body was tense. Angela didn't ask him anything. He sat still for a while, then stood, and Angela stood, and I did.

Along the Ramblas, men were washing the wide paved esplanade with hoses; they put their thumbs over the jets to make them spray. Other men swept the puddles with branch-handled brooms. We walked round the puddles, in which crushed flowers floated. On the other side of the Ramblas Vincent hailed a taxi.

We went far, and when we got out of the taxi we walked for a long time. We walked through streets with closed up buildings which might have been warehouses. The silent streets were part cobble, part dirt. The light was faint from the lamps.

At a corner, Vincent stopped. I thought he had, in the silence, heard something. He touched Angela's shoulder, but he looked back at me.

"Maybe you don't want to come," he said.

I didn't answer.

Approaching a door under a fire escape Vincent took out a key and, hardly breaking his stride, he opened the door and held it open, and Angela went in quickly. I stayed at the door. "Come on," he said. "Come on." I stepped in and he closed the door.

Dim bare bulbs showed, hanging on racks, the tanned skins of animals; there was a sharp, astringent smell. Vincent led us along the side of the room, under the hanging skins, to a door, which he opened with another key, and we climbed, noiselessly. We came out to a large room with work benches and remnants of leather on the benches and floor and crossed it to a tongue-and-groove wooden cubicle at the back of the room and a door with a palely lit transom. Vincent opened the door with yet another key and Angela, then I, followed him into the little office. Vincent sat at an old desk. We waited.

"You'd prefer not to know what we're waiting for?" Vincent asked me.

A little muscle twisted in my cheek.

"If you knew," he said, "you'd think: but this isn't any- thing—"

"Stop it," Angela said. "Stop."

Leaning against a wall, I half fell asleep.

Vincent said: "They're not coming."

"What do you think happened?" Angela asked.

Vincent seemed to be listening. He said, "We'd better go."

As swiftly as we came in, we left. Outside, we walked quickly. When we came out into a main street with globe lamps, Vincent slowed down.

"It's all over?" Angela asked.

"No," Vincent said, "not unless you want it to be."

"We'll try again?"

"If you want."

"Yes," she said, "I do want to."

I looked out at the street lamps from a taxi, at the fire escapes, the illuminated statues on plinths among dark trees. High above, the dawn was rising.

Angela woke me. I followed her out, and she followed be- hind Vincent into a hotel whose glass door was held open by a cinder block.

As we were going up the elevator, I kept my head lowered. Angela said to Vincent, "We've got to do some job. You may not need the money, but I do."

He said, "If you got any money, you'd go away."

"I don't want it for myself." She nodded her head towards me. "I want to give him his money back."

At this I raised my head.

"Do you want to go away?" Vincent asked me.

Then, lightly, he placed his hand on my nape. He kept his hand on my nape until the elevator door opened.

With his touch, I saw everything, heard everything, touched, smelled, tasted, everything, all together, in an amazing disorientation of my senses.

I followed them into a room, a big room, with strange angles to it. In one angle was a wide bed that sagged in the middle, and in another was a narrow bed. It appeared so neat, the room, I thought we were new occupants until I saw under the wardrobe a pair of shoes and on top of the wardrobe a suitcase, and I realized we'd come to where Vincent lived.

Angela said to me, "You sleep over there," and she sent me, with a touch of her hand on my back, towards the narrow bed. With the light on, I could not, in their presence, undress completely; I took off my shoes and socks and undid my belt and lay on the bed. I heard them undressing and getting into bed. That they were in bed in the same room in which I was in bed made me imagine my mind was as big as the room, and I couldn't sleep.

14

VINCENT was standing over my bed.

From the big bed, which I couldn't look at, Angela said, "Leave him alone."

"You don't have any money?" Vincent asked.

"No," I said.

His gesture was gentle. "You have to go out and get some."

"Get up," Vincent said.

Angela and I both got up. She was wearing a slip. After she used the bathroom, I did; I shut the door, but there was no lock, and, though I needed a bath, I couldn't undress because I thought Vincent might come in.

He made a signal to me when I came back into the room, and I went to him, sitting at a table. On the table was the envelope in which I kept my notes and checks. By it was a ball point pen.

He said, "You've got to sign the checks."

As he took them out of the envelope, I watched his hands, clean and strong. He placed the checks before me and I, standing, took up the pen. Over my head, he said to Angela as he picked up each signed check, "Aren't you going to get dressed so we can get out and get started again?"

Again, I found myself in a taxi. We got outside a bank with a policeman by the door. While Angela and I waited near a long, highly polished table, Vincent went to a teller, and when I saw him reach into the inside pocket of his jacket, I knew he was going to cash my checks.

At a kiosk, he bought me a map. He opened it, and, pointed to where we were and gave it to me, unfolded. He said, "Now this is where you leave us." He took Angela's arm.

Angela said, "You'll be all right, won't you?"

I said, "What about my clothes? I've got my clothes in the apartment."

"Don't come back," Angela said. "Get some money and use it to go away. Don't come back."

She stumbled against Vincent as they walked away.

I hadn't eaten. I felt dirty, and I hadn't shaved.

Immediately, I thought of going to the American Consulate, because I had heard that there you could borrow enough money to get you home. Leaning against a tree by the kiosk, I studied the map to find the Consulate, and when I located it I studied it for a long while, not really trying to make up my mind if I'd go there or not because my mind seemed already made up that I couldn't go. I studied the map for places I could go to.

When I got to the Ramblas, I felt confident enough to fold up my map. And when I saw Hal, his clothes askew on his fat body, I went to him with a sense of going to an old friend. He was standing by a flower stand, and he seemed to be waiting.

"Hi," I said, with a high, wide enthusiasm.

He shook my hand but didn't say anything.

I tried to laugh. "How about a game of craps?" I said.

He didn't laugh.

I said, "Look, you couldn't give me a little on your IOU?"

He said, "What's the matter, you broke?"

I shrugged and held out my hands and laughed again.

"How did that happen?" he asked.

"I don't know. It just happened." I asked, "Where would you go for money if you needed it?"

He said, "Why don't you ask Vincent?" Shoving his shirt into his trousers, he walked away from me. He might have been walking quickly towards someone or quickly away.

I walked down the Ramblas, and I looked at everyone. I went all the way down to the sea. High on my right was a promontory, with trees on the top, and among the trees what appeared a squat, brown fortress; a winding road went up to it. It took me a long time to climb. The fortress was a museum. It was shut. I sat on a bench under a tree.

Horses and carriages were lined up near a wall of large, brown, squared stones which continued from a corner of the museum, and tourists were examining the horses. I kept telling myself, "Go over there," but I couldn't. Some of the tourists came towards me, and I moved to the end of the bench to give them space to sit. I could tell by looking at them that they were American, two men and a woman, middle-aged. I thought, Americans were supposed to be loose limbed people, at ease with themselves, but, really, they were not. They were as these were, standing stiffly in the shade of the tree as if they were in the shade of a big person looking down at them. I didn't look at them directly, but at the shade about them. I heard the woman say, "Well, ask him," and a man say, "You ask him," and the woman say, "You ask him," and the woman say, "All right, I will," but she remained where she was. The other man said, "Aren't you going to go ask him?" "All right," the woman said. She came towards me.

"Excuse me," she said.

I squinted at her.

"Do you speak English?"

I nodded.

"Can you tell us how to ask for a bathroom?"

"Lavabo," I said.

"Lavabo?"

"Si," I said.

She went back to her male companions, saying in a loud voice, "It's lavabo." Then she must have thought she was making a scene, because she covered her mouth and turned round to me as to apologize. "Muchas gracias," she said. I nodded again. She joined her friends, and they went back to the horses and carriages; the woman talked to a driver, who motioned them into an open carriage, and they drove off. Their faces were red, as with strain, and they didn't glance towards me as they passed.

I could have gone with them. They would perhaps have taken me up as a fellow American abroad and invited me to lunch. But, as isolated as I felt, and as helpless in my isolation, I knew that I imagined I was different from them, was even superior to them, and the way I deliberately kept apart from them seemed to me an admirable, if self-destructive, act of my will. I wondered if I would ever be able to get further than that bench. I thought I might be taken as a tramp; I did not want to be taken for an American, but neither did I want to be taken for a tramp. Finally, I had to make another act of will, not admirable but self preserving, and separate myself from my embarrassment and lie full length on the stone bench. My embarrassment hovered over me, an anxious guardian angel.

Gummy-eyed, I rose from sleep and looked about. I was now in sunlight, but the shift in light was all that had changed in the plaza before the museum.

And what would happen, I thought, if I got nothing? What could he do to me?

A taxi drove up, and an elderly woman got out. She had combs in her white hair. She paid the driver and came to the bench. As if she knew me, she said, in English, "I came too early," and I said, "For what?" "For the museum to open." She sat next to me. "Have you been waiting long?" she asked. She was American. I said, "Yes. I've been waiting hours." "They close for a long time during the day," she said. She held her purse, black, on her knees. "Yes," I said, and then, eyeing her purse, it occurred to me to say, "I've had to wait because I think I lost my wallet in the museum this morning." "Oh?" she asked. I told her that I'd felt for my wallet coming out of the museum just before it closed for lunch, and found it gone; the heavy wooden door was shut, however, and I had to wait. As I said this, I thought how easy it was, and I was surprised at my sense of ease. "Are you sure you lost it inside?" She asked. "No," I said. "I'm not sure." She frowned and I smiled. The door opened, and she told me to come with her; in Spanish as rapid as I'd heard any Spaniard speak, she spoke to the guard. She said to me, "He didn't find a wallet." I said, "Perhaps he didn't look for it." She talked to him more, and, frowning more, said to me, "You can never be sure what's going on." "No, I guess not," I said. She said we'd go inside to look.

The guard wanted my ticket stub which I said I had thrown away. He insisted, and the woman raised her voice to him; he stepped back. She said to me, "I've implied to him that he found your wallet, so he's letting you in to look for it, but not at the pictures." "Tell him I won't look at one picture," I said. I had never been more false. When we returned to the door, the aged woman said, "What will you do?"

"I don't know."

"You can go to the American Consulate."

"Yes."

"And it was all you had?"

"Everything."

"The traveler's checks can be replaced, of course."

"I'm not sure I kept the serial numbers separate."

"That was irresponsible."

"Yes. As it was irresponsible to leave my wallet in my back pocket."

"You should have known that in this city."

"I guess I didn't really think about being in a foreign city."

"It can happen in many cities," she said, "even in Tulsa, Oklahoma."

"I guess."

As she opened her purse, I felt my face twitch with many different expressions; it was as if I was testing different ones, and when she handed me three ten dollar bills, I tried to keep myself from laughing.

"You'd better have this," she said. "Never mind about returning it. It'll keep you long enough to get in touch with your family back home."

I couldn't make myself take the money. She folded the bills up in her fingers and held them against my chest.

"Go on," she said.

I said, "That's too much."

"Take it."

I fumbled for it, and the moment my fingers grasped it I thought: suppose your father and mother saw you at this moment? I folded it up into my palm. I shoved the notes into my pocket and shook the woman's hand. She still frowned—now, I thought, with annoyance—and turned back into the museum, and I left.

As I walked down the hill, lightheaded, I wondered: what are you thinking? What are you feeling? I didn't know quite, because so many thoughts and feelings flashed through me, but I knew this: that I didn't want to think or feel anything, I couldn't bear to think or feel anything. Down in the city, I kept getting lost and had to take my map out. I said to myself over and over: don't think, don't feel, because if you do you'll want to die.

Somehow, I got back to the hotel. I stood for a long while before the door to the room.

Vincent was lying naked on the bed. Angela was sitting on the edge. Only she looked at me for a moment, then she turned back to Vincent, and they talked in whispers. I thought they must be talking about their job.

I felt my clothes were sticking to me. In the bathroom I undressed and quickly got into the shower, pulled over the rubber curtain, and turned on the water—cold. I tried to hurry; startled, my body threw a spasm when the curtain was drawn back by Vincent. He examined me; I did not want him to know his examination of me terrified me. I couldn't turn away. It was as if I were waiting for him to reach out and strike me. Then, I made myself not see him. I simply went on and showered as though he were not there.

He said, "Where's the money?"

I said, "It's in my trousers."

He picked up my trousers and took the thirty dollars from a pocket.

Angela came in. She said to Vincent, "You're not going to take his money."

He said, "I'm not taking his money," and as he spoke he tore up the notes into bits and threw the bits into the toilet.

Angela tried to strike him; he grabbed her wrist and twisted it, so she went down on one knee.

In the shower, I shouted, "Leave her alone!"

He said, with a slow and heavy finality, as if he were condemning her, "No, I won't leave her alone." He raised her, so she stood before him; he held her waist and led her out of the bathroom.

I trembled as I dried myself; I wrapped the wet towel about my waist and ran to my bed and threw the towel off and got inside, where I trembled more. My teeth were chattering.

The light was on. I stared up at the stained and cracked ceiling.

From the big bed came sounds which I knew had to be those of lovemaking. I trembled so that I thought they, in their lovemaking, would hear me; I didn't want them to hear me, didn't want them to be aware in any way that I was in the same room. I heard slapping sounds. I thought: if only they had shut off the light. And then I thought: the fact that they left the light on, though, means they aren't at all concerned about me, so perhaps it's better that they left the light on. The more I tried not to listen the more I heard; there was sudden silence, and when I heard Vincent call out, "Hey," I felt shock. The sheet was slipping off me because of my trembling. "Hey you," he called.

"He's asleep," Angela said.

"What?" I said.

Angela said, "Please, Vince, don't."

"I want him to see," Vincent said.

"No," Angela said.

"Yes."

Sweat was streaming through all the cracks of my body, and with the sweat came a smell I'd never smelled. Unsteadily, still trembling, I got up, and I pulled the sheet off the bed to wrap it about myself because I had an erection. The sheet trailed behind me as I went towards the bed; I stopped a distance from the foot board, over which I saw them, naked, lying apart from one another. Angela was flat, turned away. Vincent was on his elbows, and he had a large red erection.

"Stand at the foot of the bed," he said.

Vincent put his white hand on Angela's black thigh.

"No," she said. "No, I don't want to."

He pulled at her thigh and she turned over; her arm fell loosely over her head, and for a moment we looked at one another. I thought I saw her smile, and I smiled, crookedly. She turned further towards Vincent and put her arms around him and hugging him tightly, wedged her face between his neck and shoulder. She said, "Oh, Vince." Delicately, he lifted her head from his shoulder and kissed her face, her forehead, her cheeks, her nose, her chin, and her mouth, parting her lips with his tongue.

My mind, which had not dreamed in a long time, was, it

185

seemed to me, filled with half dreams, half visions of what was happening on the bed. My eyes shifted to perspective points close to, or far back, or from high or low angles.

Vincent and Angela did not look at me. I looked at myself, exposed. My thin, almost adolescent body, with pimples on my chest and shoulders, was hunched forward, and out of the opening in the sheet rose a cock-eyed erection. It was not their bodies, embracing and moving slowly about one another in their embraces, which I wanted not to see, it was my own, because I saw it as if I had stepped away from it, and it struck me as vain. My body made me a fool. I did not want to have a body. I felt my cock jerk up with a throb and viscid fluid drip down its side. If I touched it, it would come; I didn't want to come, and kept my hands at my sides. But, of course, I did want to, I did want to.

On the wide bed, the sheets tangled, the pillows shifted, their bodies contorted about one another, I saw Vincent lick, with soft laps of his tongue, Angela's breasts. I saw him suck at a nipple, and when he drew his mouth away a thread of saliva pulled between his lower lip and the tip of the nipple. He kissed between her breasts. Her neck was arched back, her eyes closed; her fingers were in his hair. Swinging his head from side to side, he licked, in little laps, down the center of her stomach. Her body writhed. Wet marks were left on her skin. On his hands and knees, above her, his head hanging loosely, lolling, he circled her navel with his tongue, then inserted his tongue in her navel, and her body writhed more.

Leaning against the foot of the bed, I raised my hands as to suddenly clutch something when, with a shudder, I ejaculated; my erection stood up and the sperm spurted up and over the foot of the bed and onto the rumpled sheet. All my spine seemed to disconnect. It was as if I fell asleep, and when I came to Vincent was still making love with Angela. I didn't know if they'd noticed what had happened to me. I stood away from the bed, and as my penis contracted and softened and dripped fluid down the inside of my leg, I continued to watch Vincent and Angela, to watch them in their lovemaking as from perspective points that were at great distances from one another.

Vincent stretched his body beside Angela's at a distance from her, and looked at it, and each part he looked at he touched with the tips of his fingers: an eyelid, an eyebrow, an arm, a thigh, a leg, her nose, the side round of her chest, her waist, her mouth and teeth and tongue, her jaw, temple, cheek, the groin and the pubic patch and the mound, the throat, an ankle and a foot and toes, a palm and fingers, ear and lobe of ear, chin, hair, hip, waist, belly, knee, elbow, neck, ribs, shoulder. It was as though he were concentrating on them all, these details, to bring them together into a body, which, then, he put his arms about. He held her closely for a long time.

I wrapped the sheet about myself.

When Vincent drew away from Angela it was to place the swollen head of his erection in the cleft of her vagina; he moved his hips so it penetrated, and I thought of the lovers in the world making love, over and over.

I went to my bed, and wrapped in my sheet, lay on it. It was as though I was seeing everything from a great depth, or from a great height, beyond what I thought or felt about anything, and what I saw moved me to pity.

I heard sudden cries as of pain come from Vincent.

The overhead light was shut off, but dawn light was rising in the room.

Again, Vincent woke me. I didn't know what part of the day it was. The sunlight filled the room. He stood by my bed. I rose up and looked for Angela.

"She went out," he said.

"Oh?"

"She went out for food and drink."

He waited by my bed. He said, "If you want to leave us, I'll give you the money." He sat on the edge of the bed. "I'll give you all your money back."

"And what about Angela?" I asked.

He blinked. After a moment, he said, "You wouldn't leave without her?"

"I don't mean that, not exactly."

"You mean she wants to go and I won't let her."

"Yes."

"And you think I should let her go."

"She should do what she wants."

"What do you think she wants?"

"I don't know," I said.

"What do you want?" Vincent asked.

I threw off the sheet and walked across the room to the bathroom. The wide bed was made, the spread stretched neatly over it. At the bathroom door, I turned to Vincent to let him see me naked. He was palpating a nipple; as if he caught me looking at him, he dropped his hand and turned away.

I had no idea how long I'd been able to sleep, if I'd slept, really. The walls of the room narrowed or elongated, became higher or lower, and shifted angles. And I caught myself staring at an object—a glass on a writing table—which would startle me for the way it came up close or went far. All of this, I knew, had to do with my not sleeping;

and as odd as my sense of space was, I was aware of the odd-
ness. I was not drugged. I do not think that anyone, the
whole time, was ever drugged. I was aware, and aware that
I was aware. When Angela handed me a fried roll on a napkin, it appeared to me that her arm reached far beyond me,
and as I tried to take the roll it withdrew far away from me,
and I thought: your mind is doing this to you. Angela sat
at the writing desk to eat. Vincent walked about. I sat in an
old, slipcovered armchair. If I tried to sleep I wouldn't be
able to; my mind would keep me awake, aware of what it
was doing.

Angela didn't talk to me, and avoided looking at me.

She said to Vincent, "I want to do something."

"We can try it again tonight," he said.

On the old writing table was a telephone. He went to it,
dialed and spoke in Spanish, and when he hung up he said
to Angela, "It's really for the money, isn't it? It's for the
money that you want to do this."

"Sure I do." Her voice rose. "Sure."

Standing over her he leaned down and kissed her on her
forehead.

He went into the bathroom to shower and shave.

I remained in the chair. Angela walked around me. Sometimes she walked heavily up a slope away from me, and
sometimes quickly down a steep slope towards me.

Finally, she asked, "How are you?"

I cleared my throat. "I guess I'll survive."

"I didn't want him to do that," she said.

"What?" I asked.

She smiled. "We won't think about it?"

"That's it, we won't think about it." I didn't smile.

Then, smiling more, she said, "Well, I don't know about

you, but I thought it was fun." And her smile broadened into laughter, which she covered with her hand.

I was silent.

She shook her head. "I'm really a bad person," she said, "really bad." And she put her hand to her mouth again to hide her laughter.

Frowning, I said, "You aren't bad."

She stopped laughing. She said, "We won't think about it."

"No."

The telephone rang; she answered and spoke in French for a while, then, glancing at me, in Spanish. All I understood from the French was that we would wait for another telephone call.

15

AFTER I showered and shaved and put on new underpants and a new shirt, I knew that if I lay down I wouldn't be able to get up. It surprised me that I wanted to stay awake for the next telephone call. And if I fell asleep and missed the call, Vincent and Angela might leave me, and I would miss the next telephone call, and the next, and what might be the result of the casual relationship of telephone calls, which I both anticipated and wanted to be put off by an infinite number of calls. After a while, sitting up, my slack sleepiness gave way to taut wakefulness.

A vibration went throughout me when the telephone rang again.

It was after dark by the time we left the hotel.

In the same way I was used to waiting for the telephone calls, I was used to riding in taxis without knowing where the taxi was going. In the taxi, Vincent and Angela spoke in what I thought had to be German. Angela said, nein, nein, a lot, but Vincent was insisting. Angela said in English, "Absolutely not. That's going too far, Vince. No." He said, "He's coming along with us, he might as well be prepared." "No," Angela said.

Vincent said to me, "You can leave us now. I'll give you all the money you want, right now, but if you stay you've got to be prepared."

"For what?" I asked.

"Stop it," Angela said. She hit Vincent on the shoulder. "Don't tell him anything. He's all right if he doesn't know, so don't tell him."

"Do you want to know?" Vincent asked me.

"No," I said.

"You should," he said.

I looked out the window, but I knew his eyes were still on me.

"Leave him alone," Angela said.

"He doesn't have to do anything he doesn't want to do," Vincent said.

"He's already seen enough."

"Have you seen enough?" Vincent asked me.

I turned to him. "No," I said, "I don't think I have."

"And what do you expect to see?"

"What's wonderful."

"Wonderful?"

"Yes."

"Leave him alone," Angela said. "Let him be."

Vincent said to her, "Why do you care?"

"Because I do. Because I don't want him to be—" she stopped.

"You don't want him to be like me?"

"I didn't say that."

"No," he said. "But you're right not to want him to be like me." He reached into his pocket and took out a stack of dollar bills, folded over and held together with a clip; he counted out some bills, slipped them from beneath the clip and handed them to me. "There's more than you had," he said.

"No, thanks," I said.

Angela said, "Take it. Take it and go. You've got your key to the apartment, so you can get your clothes, then go—" She leaned forward, to talk to me past Vincent.

"I don't want the money."

She bit her lower lip and sank back.

"We won't do the job," Vincent said.

"We've got to do the job," she said.

"No, we don't."

"We've got to."

"So you'll make some money."

Her voice rose. "No. Not for me, but for you, for you to be doing something!—" Her voice rose with anger. "Why do you think I came back? Why? I knew you'd go deeper and deeper. I'm not going to let you go deeper and deeper. We're not giving up this job!" She bared her teeth as she shouted. "No one's going to give up anything! No one! Do you hear? No one!"

The driver stopped short at a red light; we all lurched.

Vincent said, "He understands."

"Let him understand!" Angela shouted. "Let him! Let everyone understand!"

The taxi went on.

Vincent told the driver to stop, and when we got out he said, "We're not going to the club."

"I shouldn't have shouted," Angela said.

"No. You shouldn't have."

We walked slowly down the Ramblas. We passed men in uniforms with straps crossed over their shoulders and wide belts and guns hanging from holsters at the belts. As we passed them, I looked at them, and, in my odd state, I almost raised a hand in salute. Vincent, then Angela, went on ahead of me.

In a crowded, narrow street off the Ramblas, I continued to follow. Vincent held aside the fly straps over a door for Angela to go through first, then me; inside, we stood before a large gray room with dusty tuns on wooden supports behind a bar, which was a long plank on trestles, and two old gray men leaning on the bar, holding small thick glasses. Vincent went to the men to speak; one of the old men called out and a woman with a wen in the middle of her forehead came from a doorway on the other side of the bar. In Spanish, Vincent talked a long time with her and the old men. Then they were silent and seemed to wait for something to occur to one of them to speak. I watched. "Come on," Vincent said to Angela and me, and led us to a wooden table at the back of the room. A bench was along the wall side of the table and chairs along the opposite side. Vincent sat at the top, Angela on a stool at his left, and I at his right on the corner of the bench. The table top was smooth, dark, and on it was the burn of a flatiron. "Do you want a drink?" Vincent asked. "Yes," Angela said, "I want a cognac." "No," I said. A man came into the bar, the woman with the wen spoke to him and pointed to us, and the man came over. At the table, he sat at the end across from Vincent. He smiled; he had a tooth missing. Talk passed between them, and when the man put his hands on the table, paused, signed, and rose, Vincent, too, rose. "Stay here," he said, and followed the man into a room behind the bar. When he came out, Vincent had one hand inside his jacket; he sat close to the table so his belly was pressed against the edge. He drew his arm from his jacket to hold something under the table.

He said, "Take this."

I reached under the table. My hand encountered Vincent's, which was clutching an object; I put my hand under Vincent's and as, glancing about, I saw a young man my own age, a young blond foreigner, enter the bar, Vincent released the object into my hand.

I said, "This is a gun."

Vincent said, "I've just got it for you."

"I don't want it."

"You keep it."

"No," I said, "I don't want it."

My eyes fixed for a moment on the young man, who, eyes wide, was studying the room.

To Vincent I said, "No, take it back."

"I'm not going to return it."

"I don't want it."

"Yes, you do."

"I don't. Take it."

Vincent smiled. "You only want to look, is that it?"

I sat back as the young man smiled at me. I didn't smile. The young man went out.

"Did you know him?" Vincent asked.

"No."

"Why did he smile at you?"

"I don't know."

I held the gun between my knees; I had thought I'd gone beyond shock, but my hands and feet went wet-cold.

Vincent said, "Wedge it under your belt, at your hip, on your left side."

I raised my jacket, wedged the barrel between my belt and my waist, then closed my jacket over and buttoned it.

I thought: what horrors will this make you think and

feel? I felt fine chills pass over my body and tighten the skin on my thighs, shoulders, scalp.

While Angela drank her cognac, Vincent went into the room behind the bar to make a telephone call.

"We'll go out for a walk," he said when he came back.

I walked across the bar stiffly, feeling the metal angles of the gun pressing against my side. As I passed the men at the bar, I frowned. Vincent held the fly straps aside for me, and I hesitated before stepping out into the crowd in the narrow, nighttime streets. I felt I had a fever. I stayed close to Vincent and Angela.

Angela spoke in a low voice to Vincent, "What'll we do?"

"We'll walk around."

Angela asked me, "Do you want to walk around?"

Everything they said sounded to me of no importance. What we were going to do was of no importance. I rose up, high, above the streets, and looked down upon them, looked down upon myself following closely behind Vincent and Angela, and all of us walking closely among the people.

The shaded lamps hung from wires across the streets, and in their lights I saw balconies with asparagus plants and clothes hanging, and open shops with wooden boxes of grapes and pears and potatoes and onions and red peppers and little black boards with the prices chalked on them placed on the heaps of fruit and vegetables, or shops with wicker and willow baskets piled outside the doorway, or shop fronts hung with pairs of shoes and gum boots and espadrilles, and before the shops, people, vivid in the electric light. And these people knew nothing about me.

Angela said to Vincent, "Are you sure you're all right?"

"I'm all right."

"Well, we'll be all right once we get into this, really."

"Yes."

At the end of the street was a stone archway. We passed under it into a less crowded street, but as we walked, I, in my feverish state, felt myself rise higher and higher, over the quarter, over the city. The city did not know that I carried a gun, and what I could do.

On a corner were standing two men of the guardia civil. I thought they must know something was going to happen, so there were more of them out than usual; or I noticed them more than before. And I found myself taking a step towards them, and as I did they glanced at me. One had a mustache. Angela called me, and I turned towards her.

"What were you doing?" she asked.

"Nothing."

"You stopped to talk to them. You were going to tell them everything."

"No, he wasn't," Vincent said.

"I wasn't."

It occurred to me that Vincent must also have a gun on him, that he always had a gun on him when he went out, and it surprised me that I'd never noticed him put it under his belt before we went out or take it out when we came in. And perhaps Angela, too, had a gun in her patent leather purse. To them guns were ordinary. I was fearful that the gun at my side might suddenly fall out on the street paving. I thought that perhaps I did have a fever. I did not want this gun, which had been imposed on me.

I heard voices and music, and bursts of clapping; we came out onto a wide street in which there were many people walking about small, parked cars, and we went with them. We were separated by people as we got near a crowd. I pushed to stay close to Vincent. I didn't want to be separated from him. Beyond the crowd I saw the illuminated top of a carousel and, beyond, the dark smokestacks of a factory. We didn't go into the crowd, but around it to the other side, and I thought we were going to pass it; but Vincent turned to see what the crowd was gathering for. I heard more music and clapping.

From whatever high or low perspective I saw the crowd, and saw myself in the crowd. Seeing down through, deep down through, or up, high up through, all thoughts and feelings, this thought and feeling left me with a simple wonder: that we would all die, and I prayed for our helpless lives.

I saw Angela staring at Vincent, who, his back to me, was facing the crowd; her black irises round. I heard her say, "Come on, Vince come on." She was whispering, "Come on, let's get away from here. You can't make a scene here. Not with all these people around." He was unbuttoning his shirt; what frightened me was that his gun would fall out as he undid his belt. No one among the people around us noticed him. She said to me, "Try to make him stop. Try to get him to leave here and go where we're supposed to be." I went around to the other side of him; he was staring above the heads of the people and slowly unbuttoning his shirt, so his chest showed. "Come on," Angela whispered, "let's go. Don't make a scene. You know you don't want to make a scene." It was as though he were being commanded to undress, and he had to do what was commanded. Or perhaps not, because he was smiling. "Vincent," Angela said, and, as if not knowing what would happen if she reached out and touched his arm, she did so hesitantly, but as soon as she touched him he dropped his arms, a tail of his open shirt hanging from his trousers. She said, "Oh,

Vince," and stepped towards him to put her arms about him. "Come on," she said.

He said as from far back in his throat, "All right."

"We'll do what we planned to do. Everything's set up. We're being counted on. We can't let anybody down. You know that."

"Yes."

"Make an effort. You've always been able to, and you can now. Your will power is strong, you know how strong."

His voice sounded, still, far back. "All right."

She stepped away from him; he seemed to be unsteady, but he shoved his shirttail into his trousers and buttoned the buttons.

As though she had been holding her breath in, Angela breathed out. "Where do we go?"

Vincent again looked towards the crowd, and a little above it. He said, "I want to see first."

Angela said, "You've seen people doing the sardana before."

"I want to see."

She winced. "Vince, I don't like this."

"Come with me," he said.

He held out a hand, which she took, and he led her among the people, and I, turning at angles to get through the narrow spaces, followed. The air was hot with bodies and smelled of sweat and tobacco and garlic. A very fat woman carrying a little baby stepped aside for us to get nearer; I saw, over Vincent's shoulder, dancers in an open space, men and women holding hands, with handkerchiefs hanging from their clasped hands, and in the center was a man playing a shrill bagpipe. I didn't see the dancers all together, but as they passed us. From time to time people from the crowd around joined them, and the crowd had to step back, closer to one another, to give the bigger ring room. Dust rose up about the bagpipe player in the light of an overhanging street lamp.

Angela squeezed Vincent's shoulder. "Let's go."

He said, "Not yet."

"Vince."

He said, "Let's dance."

"Come on, Vince."

"We'll dance." He smiled. "Dance with me."

"We can't, Vince. We've got to go."

"Dance with me."

"I don't feel like dancing," she said.

"Yes, you do."

"I don't."

He buttoned his jacket and took her hand. He said, "And neither do I. I don't feel like dancing. But we'll do it." And he pulled her out to the ring.

"Why?" Angela said.

As he pulled her, he looked back at me. "You come, too," he said.

"I don't know how," I answered.

"Come on."

Because we were talking in a foreign language, the spectators, studying us, stepped aside to give us space. I was a short distance from the dancers, so the long hair of some of the women swung across my face as they passed. When the dancers disengaged their hands to stomp and turn in place, Angela, licking her lips, gave me her purse, then squeezed in beside Vincent among the others, and when the dancers joined hands again they joined hands with the foreigners. With her high-heeled shoes and narrow skirt, Angela sometimes stumbled a little on the bare earth, and she was not able to kick or stamp. Vincent did. The spectators were clapping. At the back of my mind, I was always fearful that his gun would fall out. Panting, some dancers left the ring and, holding glasses of wine given to them by the spectators, stared at those who continued to dance.

Something happened. The dancers stopped laughing and shouting, and the spectators stopped clapping. I saw Vincent up close when he passed by me; he was sweating and his face muscles were tense. I noted, as they passed, that he and all the dancers had the same stark expression as they moved their bodies with greater and greater energy. Only Angela looked worried, and did everything she could to keep up. The other dancers' necks were stiff, their chins held up; it was as though they were both engaged and disengaged, and the more engaged their bodies became the more disengaged their heads.

Their faces were severe, their eyes set, and I was reminded of the long dark faces of the saints I had seen in the old Catalan paintings in the museum, staring down at me as I had pretended to search for my wallet without looking up at them; I found I had not wanted to look up at them, as I didn't want, now, to look at the long, dark faces of the dancers. They, stomping, turning, appeared to elongate, and some closed their eyes; some walked out of the ring. Angela kept her eyes on Vincent. She and he were on the other side of the dancing space from me; behind them were no spectators, but the wall of an old building and iron bedsteads and bedsprings leaning against the wall. The dancers were not holding hands. Vincent was standing with his head raised and to the side, his eyes closed. Then he opened his eyes and stared. I saw Angela turn to him quickly, as if to grab him, and, just as the dancers were reaching out to grasp one another's hands to form a ring, I saw Angela step away from Vincent, who was holding a gun. The dancers lowered their hands and moved away from him.

Angela, hoarse, said, "Vincent, please don't kill. Please don't."

As he smiled at her, that crooked smile, he brought the gun up to his lips, and I turned away. I heard a shot, and heard Angela call, "Oh!" I was leaning against the shoulder of a man. I felt someone push me; it was Angela, who pushed me again. The crowd separated as she pushed me through it, grabbed her purse from me, opened it and gave me a roll of frayed notes. "Take this and go," she said, "don't run but walk quickly." She gave me another push. Leaving, I heard the crowd say, "Ah," and I knew Vincent had fallen. I went quickly into a dim side street.

16

I THOUGHT I would be followed, so I kept to the narrow streets, and I got lost; the shops and houses were shut up. Often, I found myself going up or down a street I had been through before. I went into an alley and leaned against a wall. I walked around the streets, and if I saw someone I walked slowly. When it occurred to me I had the gun on me, I knew I had to get rid of it; but there seemed no place, and I had to keep it. I came out on the Ramblas in the fine light of predawn. I went to the train station.

When I got to the sea side town, the dawn was rising. I passed the apartment house and went down to the beach. The cafés were closed and the beach was empty. I sat on the beach wall and looked out at the sea.

In the rising heat, I smelled my body through my clothes; it smelled of rot.

I studied in the beach sand the fragments of shells, of glass, of wood. They stood out vividly in the light as against darkness. The bottle cap, the coil of rusted wire, the rubber sole. I could not take my eyes off them.

I got up from the sea wall to go to the apartment. I opened the door into the empty apartment, and I felt my body was wrenched. I went into the living room, and sat.

I had to raise my body by pressing on the arms of the chair; on the way to the bathroom I stopped for long pauses to take my clothes off. I sensed a sudden sideways lunge in me, as of a wrenching force reaching out, when the gun fell out, onto the tile floor. I stood back from it, and left it where it lay in the passage outside the bathroom.

Showering, I ran my hands over my wet body.

Naked, I stepped over the gun, went to my room with my dirty clothes bunched up in my arms, and I picked among my old clothes to find the cleanest.

On the landing, going out again, I lost balance and held the stair rail; the force in me seemed to throw itself out against my ribs. I looked down the stairwell, and it came to me that my body might be knocked over the rail. I got myself to sit on the top step. I shook my head and hit it, and hit my shoulders, chest, flanks.

Out on the street, I walked close to the walls. I walked up into the town, taking side streets, and came out in the market square, empty and dusty, and I sat at a small café on a corner with tables and chairs on the cobbles. Some force in me kept trying to push out of me. I ordered a beer and a ham sandwich, and I concentrated on my eating.

I walked further up into the town, taking the narrow streets, and came out on the square facing the train station. Before it the old ox cart stood, and I went to it, behind it, and looked into the dim station filled with flies and beyond to the tracks and stationary wagons outside in sunlight. I looked for something that moved, but saw static details: a bottle submerged in a pail of water, a torn poster on a wall, a cat under the ox cart. And even when I saw a person, I fixed details: the gold earrings of a little girl carried in her mother's arms, the straw mat held over a man's head to shade him, the hands and feet of a boy in an undershirt and shorts standing with a bicycle. I saw, on the ground, a broken leather belt, a punched train ticket, a chicken feather.

I tried to turn away from what I saw by going into the station, and there I sat on a wooden bench and watched, through the doorway, the trains come in and leave.

Out on the platform, I walked up and down in the hot sunlight. Whenever a train came in I watched all the passengers get off, looking for Angela.

In the light there were no shadows, not even under my feet as I walked. I couldn't make myself go quiet. I went through the station and into the square and down into the town.

I came out on the sea front, and I went past the cafés and hotels and villas, and at the headland of rocks stopped. I sat on the rocks and took off my sandals, then remained sitting for a while.

Barefoot, I climbed up onto the rocks. The rocks were rough and shelved in ledges; when I looked back I saw, not the town, but the broken ledges of the headland against the sky. A hot wind blew in from the sea. In the brilliant white light, it seemed to me that there was nothing around me. I studied, on the rocks, the shriveled sea weed, the shells, the pebbles, and as I studied them they faded into the glare, which was as stark as darkness; and then the glare revealed them intensely, each shred of sea weed, each shattered shell, each round pebble. I was not sure if the details, unbearable, made my eyes go out of focus to see the glare or, suddenly, the dark that the glare in an instant became; or if the glare and dark, unbearable too, forced me to focus on the details. Everything was black and white. I could not look for long.

On the other side of the headland was a narrow cove and a whitewashed stone hut in a cleft in the rocks above the cove. Uneven stone steps led from the grey door of the hut down to a small beach. The whitewash was in patches. I walked towards it. Often I had to put my hand up to my face to shade my eyes. The heat strained. I reached the door. It was locked. Dry salt burned about the rims of my eyes. In its straining heaviness, the heat groaned, and went silent. I closed my eyes, but that was more painful, and I opened them and walked around the hut.

Against the back wall, in angles of shadow and bright light, stood out a round metal table, green, and on it were two lemons and a knife and a glass.

For awareness, for awareness and the joy of awareness, tears came to my burning eyes.

17

I woke sometimes in darkness, sometimes in light, over
and over, it seemed to me, and each time I fell back to
sleep it was to fall deeper, and each time I woke it was to
rise higher. When I woke, I was startled, and looked around
me, and when I fell asleep I was startled, too, and perhaps I looked around in my sleep. Slowly, the sinking and
rising became less and less, and when I woke and felt I
was on an even level, I sat up. I had no idea how long I
had been in the bed. The sheets were moist with sweat;
the light was hot and full in the room.

As I passed through the living room I saw Angela in the
armchair, her legs folded under her, her head resting on
an arm; she was asleep, her mouth a little open and trick-
ling saliva across her cheek. She wore the clothes she'd
been wearing when I last saw her, now wrinkled and dusty.
Her hair was wild.

The gun was gone from the passage. I used the bathroom and, in the kitchen, drank cold water I found in a
bottle in the refrigerator. I pressed the bottle to my chest.
I went into the living room and sat on the sofa and waited
for Angela to wake.

She simply raised her head a little from the arm of the chair, and, frowning, looked at me for a long time. It was as if she was trying to make out who I was.

Her voice thick, she said, "I thought you had gone."

"No."

She lowered her head to the chair arm.

Her body was folded up awkwardly; she shifted it a little, and she raised a hand and looked at that, turning it about slowly in the light as she studied her hands. She dropped them.

She said, "You've got to go away."

"I can't."

"Don't tell me that." She frowned. "You've got to."

"I can't."

Still frowning, she closed her eyes slowly, then opened them quickly. "You mean because you don't have the money?"

"No."

"I'll get you the money."

My voice jumped. "I didn't mean that."

"I'll get the money for you and you'll go. You leave everything up to me."

"I don't want to."

"You'd better get ready," she said .

"Now?"

"Right now. Pack while I pack."

"You're going too? Where are you going?"

"I don't know," she said.

She got up and went out of the room. I went out on the balcony until she came out again, and said, "Put your clothes on then pack," and I followed after her.

I had to wear dirty socks and dirty underwear, and a dirty shirt beneath my summer suit.

Angela was standing on the balcony. By her was a suitcase and a traveling case. She had left everything else. Perhaps she would come back. I took up her suitcase in one hand, mine in the other, but put them down at the door she held open. I tried to put my arms about her, but she turned away and went out.

I wanted to weep.

There were American sailors asleep in the lobby of the hotel Angela took me to, and some, awake, were talking gently to a fat woman. From the reception desk where Angela rang the bell, she and I looked at the sailors. A man came through a slit in the curtains behind the reception desk.

"Do you want me to ask for one room?" Angela asked.

"Yes, please."

In the large square room with a high ceiling, Angela stood by the window. She said, "It'll be dark soon." She pulled the net curtain aside.

By the door, I said, "Yes."

She kicked off her high-heeled shoes and went to the bed and lay on a side of it. She put her hands under her head. I went to the side of the bed opposite her and sat on it. The window shone gray through the net curtains. She pulled herself up and sat. Her hand to her forehead, she stuck her little finger out; then she lowered her hand and suddenly her face contorted. She said, "Oh Vincent," and tears rose into her eyes. I clutched her shoulders; she pulled a little away from me, then gave in, and I held her as I fell asleep.

She woke me. "I've got to go," she said.

"I'll come with you."

"No. You'll wait here."

"No, no, don't go out. Don't."

She put on her shoes without reaching down, but wriggled and stamped her feet into them. Before she left, she smoothed her hair again.

Holding the door beyond which I was frightened to go, I said, "Don't go. Please don't go."

I lay on the big uneven bed. Beyond the wall I heard voices, a man and a woman; I heard the bed creak, and noises of lovemaking.

I did not want to leave Spain. I rose, opened my suitcase, and had to take out half the clothes before I found Madame Alberti's letter at the bottom. The envelope was addressed care of a hotel, the name and address on the envelope were written in capitals. I folded the letter and put it into my pocket.

I was writing a letter at the narrow, cheap table when Angela came in, and I closed the cover of the writing block over my writing. I stood.

"Are you all right?" I asked.

She asked, "How long have I been away?"

"I think about six or seven hours."

"I got your money." She opened her purse.

I swallowed.

She came to the desk and laid on the writing block the money, in American dollars. A lamp with a metal shade shone on them.

"The police took all of Vincent's money," she said.

I swallowed again.

"What were you writing?" she asked.

"A letter."

"Who to?"

I hesitated. "My parents."

"Your parents?" She looked about. "Did you tell them where you are?"

"I told them I'm in Spain."

Angela laughed a little. "You never told me about your parents," she said, "about your family, about anything."

"I guess not."

Her face suddenly twitched, and she turned away.

"Let's go," she said when she turned back, "let's get you to the train station."

From the taxi, the city, illuminated in the early morning, was familiar.

Angela said, "You'll still have a few weeks in Paris before your studies begin."

"I'm not going to Paris," I said. "I'm going to stay in Spain."

"You can't."

"Yes, I can."

"The police will be looking for you."

"I don't care. I'm going to stay."

"Where will you go?"

I shrugged.

"You can't stay," she said.

"I'll do what I want."

She sat back and folded her arms.

The taxi stopped. It was only when she said, "Let's get out," that I was able to move.

At a ticket window in the station, I asked for a ticket to

Almería, but there were none. I did not understand what the ticket seller told me, except that I could not go direct to Almería. I understood that I was able to get a ticket only as far as Tarragona. I bought one, second-class.

At a café near the station, Angela and I had coffee. Her face twitched; once it twitched with the cup to her lips, and the coffee sloshed. I patted her dress with a paper napkin.

Through the window, in the outward illumination from the inside of the café, I saw a woman carrying a baby. Her hair was bleached and piled high, and her brutal face was made up with only black about the eyes. The baby was trying to reach into her dress at the bodice and she, not looking at it, slapped its hands away; she was looking through the window at me.

The woman hefted the baby up onto her shoulder and came into the café, which was empty except for Angela and me; she walked among the tables.

I leaned toward Angela. "Who is she?"

"A crazy whore."

"Will she go away?"

"Not without something, no."

Swinging her wide hips, the woman walked round our table, then towards it. Her worn high-heeled shoes made her bowlegged.

Angela smiled crookedly at me. "She's after you."

"Doesn't she see I'm with you?"

Angela said, "She thinks I'm just another whore."

The woman stopped before me and propped the baby on an out-thrown hip.

"Tell her to go away," I said; "please tell her."

But Angela opened her purse on her lap and unfolded from it some pesetas, which she held out to the woman, who swung her body with the baby, from side to side, and blankly contemplated the money.

I said, "What does she want?"

Angela put the hand with the money to her cheek as if to keep her face from twitching more. She kept her hand on her face for a long while, and when she lowered it, it was to reach quickly into the open purse for a roll of money. She held it out in her open palm, so peseta notes unrolled from it and fell to the ground; as she leaned to gather them together in one hand, the bills in the other hand continued to unroll. She held them, at all angles to one another, in both hands out to her and spoke to her in Spanish. The woman stepped back. Crushing the money together, Angela rose and held it out, but the woman took another step back. Angela said something in Spanish. The baby began to cry. Angela spoke more in Spanish, in a low voice. The woman tried to stop the baby from crying by shaking it. Close enough to her to touch her, Angela dropped the money, and the woman, holding the crying baby against her, reached down, piled the bills together on the dirty wooden floor, picked them up and went out quickly. The baby was still crying. Angela wiped her forehead with the side of a hand.

"You'll have to pay for the coffees with some of the pesetas you got for the dollars at the hotel," she said.

"I can't leave you like this."

"You can."

"I'll give you half the money."

"You'd better go now and get your train," she said flatly.

On the station platform I saw her turn away from me and put her hands to her face, which suddenly became deformed.

I stood at an open window of the train, she on the platform. She looked often up and down the platform as if for someone. When she said, "Quick, give me a few pesetas," I reached some frayed bills to her and she ran away, but came back a moment later with a large bottle of mineral water topped with a cork and she handed it to me. The train began to move.

She wasn't looking at me, but away, as if she had seen someone, and I leaned out the window. Her lower lip extended, she looked down at her feet. Then she began to jive. The narrow platform got longer, and I saw other people were watching Angela, who waved both arms high up until I could no longer see her.

Alone in a second-class compartment, I counted my money.

Part Three

I

At the Tarragona station, I spoke in French to a man who said that to get to Almería I must first go to Valencia, and gave me the times of the trains. I left the station with my bag and crossed the street to a café where it was hot and the ceiling fans were not working. I stood at the bar, which was covered with dust, and asked for a cerveza. The bar woman, thin and white, in a dry dusty black dress, didn't understand me. I repeated. She frowned. I repeated, showing my teeth, "Cerveza." Frowning, she brought me the bottle of beer and a glass. I drank, paid, picked up my bag and went into the hot August afternoon. I walked slowly up the cement steps from the station to the Ramblas, wide and lined on both sides with palm trees in wooden tubs, and I walked slowly down it, to where it ended in a plaza with a bronze statue of a general on a horse and a low wall. Beyond the wall was the sea. In the plaza I sat at an outdoor café to have another beer and to eat a sandwich jamón.

I sat facing the sea. It was black blue. It appeared to be a dark flat plane, vertical, against which stood the sunlit statue and palm trees.

The Foreigner

The sun was still up when I went to the harbor. I walked past many houses with Habitaciones painted in black on the front, and made myself go into one. My room was small and had an enamel basin on a stand in one corner and an enamel bidet in another corner. I lay on the bed. The late sunlight shone about the edges of the closed curtains. I rose from the bed and opened the curtains.

In the town, I took a walkway, arbored with a vine, up to a ruined castle, and from the ramparts of the castle looked down at the roofs and walls with shadows against the plane of the sea.

I read the menu outside a restaurant, but could not make myself go in.

When it was dark, I went back to my room, undressed and got into bed.

With a start, I woke. I heard my mother and father talking in their bedroom, next to mine. I could hear their voices.

In the morning, a sharp wind blew. I walked through the wind to the station where I found a long line at the ticket window, closed, behind the grille, by a wooden shutter. I joined the line and put the bag between my feet. Fifteen minutes before the train was to arrive the shutter opened and the line pressed forward. The people who got tickets went out on to the platform with their rope-tied bags, cardboard boxes, baskets. I shuffled closer to the window, and looking past the three people before me saw the shutter slam. The person in front of me, an old woman in a wrinkled black suit, turned to me, set her mouth, and went off.

I said to myself, "What happened?"

I stood among people going out for the train.

The consigna where you could leave your luggage was shut, so I had to carry my bag. In the dusty bar across from the station I sat at a corner table and had coffee, bread and butter and jam. I sat for a long while after the empty cup and the plate and knife were cleared. Outside, the wind blew up dust in the street.

Again, when I went to the station, there was a line. I was early, though, and after I joined the line other people did too. Shifting my weight from foot to foot, I waited; I looked often at my watch. A short time before the train was due, the ticket window opened. It closed in the face of the woman standing in front of me. People moved about me, but I for a time did not move.

I walked up and down the Ramblas. Hungry, I felt I could not make myself go into a restaurant. But I must eat. The meal and the wine made me sleepy. I could hardly focus when I counted out the money on to the saucer, and as I went out of the restaurant I lurched with the weight of my bag. I did not know which way to go. The wind had stopped.

At three o'clock I returned to the station. I had an hour and a half to wait for another train, and I was third in line. The shutter did not open.

A little nauseated, I sat on a bench in the station. My body tensed when I saw a young man, three hours before the train was to come, take a place before the shuttered ticket window, and I took a place behind him. The light and the heat in the outside stillness were thickening. The young man kept looking round at me; he was thin, and wore a suit. I was in a short-sleeved shirt, slacks, and sandals. The young man asked me something which I understood to be, "Where are you going?" and when I said,

"Almería," the young man pressed his lips together and stuck them out and said, "C'est loin, c'est très loin."

We talked in French.

A line formed behind us. As the time approached for the shutter to open, my body tensed more. The shutter didn't open; with a shuddering burst, the train passed the station.

"Why?" I asked the young man.

The young man, who was a student, made a face.

He invited me to have a beer with him at the bar across from the station. The student held out his thumb. He explained to me how to hitchhike.

In the room, I lay sweating on the bed. As it got dark, I fell asleep; but I woke from time to time with a jerk. When it came to me where I was, I rubbed my body hard.

I missed the local train to Salou, where I would start to hitchhike, and, again, waited in the Tarragona train station. The still heat brought out flies; they settled on my neck, cheeks, forehead, and on my hands as I tried to brush them from my head. A woman and a boy, at the end of the long bench I sat on, let the flies settle on them, and only blinked, and I stopped trying to keep the flies off myself.

When I got out at Salou, I went from the station, past rough stone buildings, to a country road. On one side of the road, beyond parched fields, were twisted red mountains, and on the other side of the road, beyond the low and eroded headlands, was the sea. Cactus plants grew along the road and cast spiky shadows. Changing my bag from hand to hand, I walked. I was not sure this was the road I should be on, or if I was going in the right direction. I often turned round to see if a car was coming along. When I saw an advancing cloud of dust, I stood to the side and held out my thumb. As an old truck passed me a woman sitting next to the driver pointed down, and I guessed that she meant that they were stopping soon. I walked on. I walked round a mountain about which the road curved, and beyond which the landscape was vast; the mountains were high and far back, and the open land before them was covered with great boulders, and, on the sea side, the sloping land was, too, covered with enormous boulders. At times, though, they appeared to me small, and the mountains not high and far but low and near. Distorting heat waves rose from the tarred and oiled road; the smell rose. Another truck came along and stopped, and the driver leaned over to open the door for me to get in. The driver's hands were stubby and calloused; he said, only, that he was going twenty kilometers, or so I understood, and drove the rattling truck in silence. The windshield was covered with dust which, because of the vibrations of the truck, was striated; the striations shifted. The truck stopped before turning off into a dirt road, and I jumped down and slammed the door.

The road went through countryside that was flat; the road was straight, so, before me and behind me, it disappeared to points, and glared. I was weak from lack of food and water. The bag was heavy.

I was picked up by an American in a rented car who was driving all the way to Valencia. The American was bald. He didn't ask me where I was from.

The American said, "You just traveling around?"

"Yes," I said.

Hot wind blew in the open window.

"Alone?"

"Yes, alone."

"I'm not sure I'd travel on my own in this country."

"Why?"

"You never know."

By the side of the road two women were selling grapes. The grapes were piled on an old door laid across benches. The American stopped the car beyond them and got out. I got out, too. As we approached, a woman held up a large bunch of grapes.

"Let me buy," I said.

"No," the American said, "I will."

"But you're giving me a lift."

"No, I will."

I stood away as the American paid one woman while the other wrapped the great bunch of grapes in newspaper. In the car, he placed the bundle on the seat between us and opened the newspaper. The grapes were large, bright; some were crushed, and juice oozed from them.

"Help yourself," the American said.

I broke off a small bunch. The grapes were filled with cool liquid, I put a number in my mouth and ate them together, swallowing the seeds. The liquid rose out on my lips.

The American started the car.

"Aren't you going to have any?" I asked.

"I bought them for you."

"Why?"

"I thought you'd like them."

I said, "Thanks."

On the outskirts of Valencia the road widened and was divided by trolley tracks and trees. The American pulled up at a trolley stop and told me he was not going into the center of the city.

At the train station I asked, in French, for the next train

to Almería. It was at nine o'clock in the morning. I asked if I could buy a ticket. "Bien sûr," the ticket man said. I asked for a second-class ticket, but there was no second-class on the train, only first and third. I bought a third-class ticket, and examined it carefully in the late sunlight outside the station to make sure it was for Almería.

In a hotel near the station I took a room with a bath, and I lay in the lukewarm water. My body tingling, I washed my socks and underwear.

The hotel restaurant was still empty, though to me it was late. I ate a tortilla, paella, a thin veal steak with fried potatoes, a salad; I drank a bottle of wine.

It seemed to me my skin was taut and smooth, and sometimes I reached into my shirt to touch my body.

I walked along the street, lit by globes, crowded with Spaniards taking their evening paseo. Sometimes I bumped into them, and I felt the momentary impact of their bodies on mine, and I retained the impact. The strollers crowded about me.

I left them by turning into a quiet side street, and as I walked I imagined, at moments, that my body stepped out from me into a space and walked beside me, and I could reach out and touch it.

Back in the crowd, I imagined, more, that my body was outside me in the crowd, and I bumped into it.

I couldn't sleep. I twisted and turned in the sheet, which wrapped about me. Then I was not sure if I was asleep or awake. When I woke, not sure where I was, I rubbed my body. I rubbed my chest, my thighs.

I was waiting on the platform for the train at eight o'clock. Passengers gathered about me. When, a little before nine, the train came into the station, the passengers ran to open the doors before it stopped; bags and bundles raised above their heads, they struggled to get on against the passengers getting off. Women shouted. By the open windows, suitcases and boxes were handed out of the train and handed in. A man held up a cage of chickens to another man who took it in. I hung back and looked down the platform; I ran to the end of the train where the crowd was less, and boarded after a fat woman was helped up the metal steps by a man pulling her by the arms.

Boxes were piled outside the w.c., and people were sitting on the lower ones. My bag held against me so my knees kicked it as I walked, I went down the corridor alongside the compartments; the corridor was crowded, and as I went I looked into each compartment, where, in thick cigarette smoke, the Spaniards sat pressed together. There was no space to stand in the corridor. I pressed my way through and came to the w.c. at the other end of the carriage, and, among others, I was able to stand by a dirty window.

The train was shunted. The passengers lurched. A woman grabbed my shoulder and laughed; I smiled at her.

I pointed down to the floor of the train. "Almería?" I asked.

The woman frowned. "Almería?"

I frowned too.

The woman turned to talk to the man next to her. They had a long discussion. Then she turned to me and said, "Sí, Almería."

"Muchas gracias," I said. I turned a little away from her.

The train was stationary. I heard steam hissing, and metallic clinking, and I thought the train was about to start, but the hissing and clanking stopped, the train remained stationary. I was sweating. A voice over a loudspeaker on the platform made an announcement which I did not understand, but as no one reacted to it I imagined it was to say the train was departing. The train remained still, and, in the heat, the passengers settled into the stillness. A bell rang and I thought it must be a signal for the train to go, but it didn't go. I tried to open the dirty window; it wouldn't open. In the hot still silence I heard a whistle. I stared at the gray concrete platform through the dirty glass. Another bell sounded, a tingling bell. I continued to look out at the platform, where, in the bright light, was a crate. After a long silence the crate moved; it was the train, which moved very slowly out of the station.

2

O N the wall by the w.c. was a large map of Spain. I went to it to study it. I felt the train shake. I found Tarragona and, down the coast, Valencia, and down further, Almería. Valencia was, on a curve, halfway. As it had taken me eight hours to get from Tarragona to Valencia hitchhiking, it could not take more time, I thought, had to take less, to get from Valencia to Almería by train. Almería was just across from Africa.

I went back to my place by the window, at the end of a row of people; they clung to the bar across the window. A man came to use the toilet, and I had to move as he was not able to open the door. A smell of shit and urine came from the w.c. when he went in. After three people came to use it, I picked up my bag and left.

The woman by the window said, "Adiós." Her smile was large, with a tooth missing.

"Adiós," I said.

I worked my way towards the back of the train. The train rocked, and I had often to reach for a wall to keep myself from falling against others in the corridor, some standing, some seated on their suitcases. As I worked my way along, I saw, out the window, dry land and sky.

Outside a crowded compartment I found an empty space. The space was as wide as the window. I dropped my bag under the window, opened it, and leaned out to let the hot air rush over my head. Then I stood by the window and looked out.

A wrinkled man, wearing a frayed white shirt and a beret, came out of the compartment and stood by me. I was not attentive to him until the man offered me a cigarette. I shook my head. "No," I said, "no," and I held two fingers up to my lips. "No?" the old man said. He lit a cigarette. He smelled of sweat and tobacco. He kept his eyes on me. "Inglés?" he asked. "Americano," I said. The man smiled. "Americano?" "Sí." The man asked me something, and I said, "No hablo español." "No habla?" "No." Smoking, the man looked at me. His face was wrinkled; his narrow eyes were light. I smiled, and the man took the cigarette from his mouth and smiled. The man pointed to the middle of his chest. "Antonio," he said.

I understood the man to ask where I was going.

"Almería."

The man nodded.

"Well, I'm on the right train," I said.

"Cómo dice?"

"Nada."

The man spoke. I hunched my shoulders. The man took my elbow and brought me to the entrance of the compartment, which was dim, and in the dimness I saw large and small passengers pressed together who all looked at me. The old man pointed to an empty seat, pointed to himself, pointed to me, and pointed again to the seat. I raised my hands. "Sí, sí," the man said, and pushed me towards the seat. I sat. He stood at the door. No one moved. On the racks above were newspaper wrapped bundles, chickens with their legs tied, baskets with stalks and roots.

Indicating me with his head, the old man Antonio announced to the others, "Americano."

I looked down.

A woman across from me, who wore a flowered dress and a black apron, spoke rapidly to me. Antonio spoke to her, and she stopped speaking and stared at me.

Together, the other people in the compartment spoke. An elderly man in a corner said something to a young woman by his side who might have been his daughter, and she said to me, "Vous ne parlez pas l'espagnol, mais parlez vous français?"

"Oui."

"Je ne parle pas très bien."

"Vous parlez très bien," I said.

Antonio spoke to her, and she said to me in French, "He wants to know what you do in America."

"I study."

"I study also," the young woman said, "I want to teach. I would like to know English and to teach English."

"Why?"

"That is the language everyone speaks," she said. "Then I can go to America."

"I'll teach you," I said.

The young woman translated and everyone in the compartment laughed. The elderly man, next to the young woman, stared at me.

"You must teach me Spanish," I said.

When this was translated, everyone, again, laughed. The

228

woman in the black apron spoke in a high voice, her mouth open, and everyone laughed at her joke.

The young woman translated from the seven other passengers many questions and translated back to them my replies: was it far to America? In America—?

I looked at my watch. I got up from my seat to let Antonio have it back, but Antonio shook his head. "No, no," I said, and I left the seat. As Antonio sat, a tall gaunt man by the door rose. He beckoned me to him and putting his hands on my shoulders he pressed me into the seat, where the springs showed under the worn plush.

Through the young woman, this man, standing over me, said, "You've got a watch. All Americans have watches."

I covered the watch with my right hand.

A large woman across from me shouted at the tall gaunt man. She had a black kerchief tied about her head. The tall gaunt man turned away.

Next to her sat an old woman who also had a black kerchief about her head, which was sunk into her shoulders. She smiled at me, and her toothless gums showed.

The tall gaunt man said something to the large woman in the black kerchief, who, from a cloth covered basket at her feet, took out a bottle of wine and a tin cup. She poured wine into the cup and handed it to me. I raised it to everyone, drank, and handed the cup back; the woman poured more wine into it and gave it to her husband. The tin cup of wine was passed around, and the only one to decline, his hand raised against it, was a young man at the window next to Antonio; the little finger of his raised hand had a long crooked nail.

I got up to let the tall gaunt man have his seat back, but

he protested, "No, no," and he gestured as to push me into the seat again. "No, no," I said, and I went out of the compartment.

At the window, I watched the low bare hills. On the sides of many, facing the sun, were spread great squares of red peppers drying on sacks.

I turned when the young man with the long fingernail tapped me on the shoulder and made me take his seat by the window. The young man shook my hand and left. The elderly man who might have been the father of the young woman said something to her, and she asked me, "How do you say in English—?" I told her and asked, "How do you say that in Spanish?" Others in the compartment listened to us. The train went slowly, swaying, and we were rocked from side to side. After what seemed to me a long while I asked the young woman, "Where is the man whose seat I have?" "He's gone," she said. "Gone? Gone where? The train didn't stop." She shrugged.

The woman with the black apron unwrapped on her lap layers of newspapers, and the layers became greasier till, in the last, she unwrapped a pile of oily rolls. She picked up one and handed it to me with the tips of her fingers. I said "No, thank you," and she insisted, and I took it. I waited until she had offered to others, who declined, then bit into one herself before I bit into mine: it was a fried roll stuffed with vegetables. The woman with the black kerchief got up to take a bundle down from the luggage rack. Antonio searched in a satchel for a sausage and a thick slice of bread. The young woman opened a small wicker basket. Before anyone ate, he offered whatever he had to the others, and each one forced on me food: a piece of sausage, a roll, an apple. The tin cup was passed round and round.

As we ate and talked in loud voices the train stopped. The train stopped in desert. The desert was wavering in the heat. We finished eating, talked, but less loudly. Some lay their heads back and, arms folded and bodies twisted a little, slept. Finally, no one spoke. The young woman's face, perspiring, went blank; she closed her eyes. Outside the wavering desert blazed. When the young woman opened her eyes I asked her, quietly, "What is happening?" "I don't know," she said. She closed her eyes again.

The shadows of rocks began to lengthen across the sand.

When the train started again, everyone woke, but no one talked. The air in the compartment was dense with heat. The old toothless woman fanned herself with a black fan. The train went slowly. It was silent, and the silence was as dense as the heat.

From the corridor there came singing, a thin, high, high, wailing singing. A little girl, a gypsy, appeared at the door, her hair stuck up about her thin dark face. She stood by the door and sang; her wailing went higher and higher, and she shook her head as to make it rise. No one looked at her. The tendons of her neck stood out as she sang. Her large black eyes searched the compartment. I reached into my pocket and she stopped singing and went to me with her hand out, but closed into a fist; when I held a coin over it, she opened her hand, then closed it tightly over the dropped coin. She ran out.

The long silent train proceeded through the burning country.

The heat became prickly, and the passengers moved listlessly in their seats. Sometimes they spoke to one another. Mostly, their eyes closed, they were silent.

I sucked at the sides of my mouth.

In a low voice, the young woman seemed to dare herself to ask me, "In America, you had a civil war?"

"Yes."

"Do you remember it?"

"It was a long time ago. No, I don't remember. Do you remember your civil war?"

"No," she said.

The woman in the black apron began to laugh. She pointed the index finger of one hand at me, and that of the other at the young woman, and, laughing, she brought them together, hitting her swollen knuckles against one another. The others opened their eyes. They spoke rapidly, and laughed.

The train stopped again. Its shadow was spread out sideways onto the barren landscape, and the shadow had windows and the shadows of figures in the windows.

I heard someone say, "Madrid," then someone else said, "Madrid," and yet another, in a long convolution of words, said, "Madrid." I sat forward. I asked the young woman, "Does this train go to Madrid?" "Yes," she said. "Doesn't it go to Almería?" "No," she said. I stood. "No? But I thought I was going to Almería." She spoke to the others; Antonio answered, and she said to me, "You must get out before Madrid and get another train for Almería." "What?" "Yes, that is what this gentleman says. If you stay on this train, you'll go to Madrid." I sat back.

"What is the matter?" the young woman said.

"I think I have taken the wrong train," I said.

"No," she said. "This is the way to go to Almería. You get down outside Madrid and you take another train."

"I don't know what to do," I said in English.

"Qué?" Antonio asked.

Through the young woman, the elderly man said to me, "Come with us to Madrid."

"Madrid?"

"Yes."

"I must get to Almería," I said.

"Why?"

"I must."

The young woman said, "My uncle says you are a good boy."

"Thank him," I said, "thank him for saying that."

When the train stopped at the station of Alcazar de San Juan, I did not want to get down; I wanted to stay with my new friends and go on to Madrid.

"Get out," Antonio said through the young woman, "and I'll pass your bag out of the window."

I shook all their hands. They stood, even the old woman. I hurried along the crowded corridor and jumped out. It was strange to stand on the unmoving ground. I ran to the window where Antonio, leaning out, was holding my bag in the air, and I took it from him. The others, too, were at the window. I waited. They waved as the train pulled out, and I waved.

Alone, I went into the station. It was late afternoon, and the small station was deserted. The one man I found said the train to Almería would come in five hours, and he made me understand that, with my ticket, I was not allowed to leave the station. As I waited on a bench on the platform, the sun set. With the darkness came cold. I zipped open my bag for socks, which I put over my dirty feet; I searched, too, for a sweater, and pulled it on. I walked back and forth before the station café, whose light shone out on the platform. Men at small tables were playing cards. I could not make myself go in. The men left, and I went in, and at one of the tables strewn with cards I drank coffee and ate stale pastries. I put my elbows on the edge of the table and my jaw in my hands and I closed my eyes.

An hour before the train was due I went out to the platform, as I was frightened of missing it. Trains stopped. I watched the trains go out into the darkness.

No one else at Alcazar de San Juan got on the train to Almería, but, on the train, people were sleeping side by side on the floors of the corridors, and the blinds of the compartments were all drawn. I walked through carriage after carriage, and woke passengers.

At the end of a corridor two young men, smoking, were close together and talking, and as I passed between them one of them spoke to me. I turned quickly to see a face with a broken nose and a thin smile. The young man's skin was white, his shirt unbuttoned on his neck and chest.

I understood that the young man was telling me that there were no seats on the train.

"Inglés?" the young man asked, and his voice came from a distance.

"Americano." I heard my voice from a greater distance.

The young man motioned to me to follow him.

"Dónde?" I asked.

The young man took my bag. I followed. The other young man came behind.

"Give me my bag," I said. "Give it to me."

The Spaniard did not understand me. He brought me to the rear of the carriage, where, gathered, were a woman and two men, talking and passing a flask. The young man put my bag down among them, and, in an enthusiastic voice, he spoke, often turning to me, and I heard, "Americano."

234

The woman said to me in English, "Where do you go?"

"Almería."

"Almería?" She stuck out her chin. "You do not go before, Almería?"

"No."

She kept her chin stuck out. She had long black hair, and hair on her upper lip. She said, pointing to a man wearing a long-sleeved woolen undershirt, "He go to Almería."

"We get off together then," I said.

A pungent smell came from the w.c. when its door opened. A thin man emerged. He wore a wrinkled suit, too big for him, and no shirt under the jacket. He reached for the flask and took a long drink from it. In the murky light, I saw that his hairline was low on his narrow forehead and hair grew in tufts high on his cheeks. His eyes appeared to be at the sides of his head. He wiped the back of his hand across his mouth and smiled; his teeth were small, separate, and pointed. He said something, took another swallow, then passed the flask to me. I did not want to drink, but I smiled a little at the others, lifted the flask with a jerk of my arm, and drank cognac. I gave the flask to the woman.

"In America," she said, "all are criminals."

"No," I said, "there is another America."

The man with the pointed teeth lay down on his side on the floor by the w.c. and folded his arms and raised his knees. He snored.

The train stopped and the man in the long-sleeved woolen undershirt took my arm.

"Is this Almería?" I asked.

"No," the woman said.

"Then why do we get off here?"

"You get off. He take you to Almería."

The Foreigner

I pulled away from the man. "No, I stay on."

"You get off, change train to go to Almería."

"Change trains?"

"Yes. This train no goes."

"I don't understand."

"You get off. Get off. Take other train." She opened the metal door, which swung out. The man in the undershirt hurried down the steps with my bag, and I went quickly after him. "Good-bye," the woman called. "Good-bye, America."

Stumbling, I followed the man with my bag to another platform, where, under a single light, people were waiting, their backs to the cold wind. A cock crowed, then, farther away, another. I was numb; I could not reply to the gestures of the man who carried my bag, but walked a little way from him. I listened to the cocks. I shivered.

A dark train pulled up to the platform and the Spaniard called, "Aye," to me, and I walked towards him slowly. At the back of the steam engine was the glow of a boiler furnace, which lit a small open coal car behind; there were three narrow carriages with high wheels. I followed the man, who carried my bag into a carriage. A kerosene lamp showed dark people sitting on rows of wooden seats. The Spaniard stood by a seat to let me go in first; he hefted the bag onto the overhead rack, sat beside me, and didn't try to talk. I shivered.

When the train started, my shivering left me. Out of the window, I looked at the darkness, in which occurred darker shapes. I thought the train was going through mountains. It stopped often. In the light of kerosene lamps held by men at their work, I saw water tanks. The steam engine was stopping for water. In the darkness, the lamps illuminated,

236

too, a horse, a tree, a stone hut with a straw roof. The train went on, and I closed my eyes and rested my head against the glass.

Someone shook me, and I woke. I was drooling and my lashes were sticky. The man next to me on the wooden seat smiled and pointed towards the window, and I turned, and, with a shock, I saw a mountain in sunlight.

Outside the station in Almería, two horse carriages were parked at a TAXI sign. From between the pages of my diary I removed the letter and examined the address.

Two civil guards were standing at the corner of the station. One was looking at me. I knew I appeared dirty, with matted hair and beard stubble. As long as the guard kept his eyes on me I kept mine on him, frowning. He talked to the other guard. I, half dragging my suitcase, went to them, and, my heart beating with excitement, I held the letter out to them. The first one took it from me.

"Dónde?" I asked.

They read the envelope together, and they talked. The second guard said something to me. I shrugged my shoulders. I could feel my pulse beating in my neck. I kept my face tense so I wouldn't smile with excitement. The first guard gave the letter back to me with his long fingers, then pointed to a horse carriage and said, "Taxi." I nodded. They turned away from me as I, grasping the letter in one hand and lugging the suitcase in the other, limped away.

I rode high on the rocking back seat of the open carriage, down a wide street lined with palm trees.

David Plante is the author of the Francoeur Trilogy (*The Family*, *The Country*, and *The Woods*) and several other novels, and the non-fiction book *Difficult Women*. He has been the recipient of a Guggenheim Fellowship and an Award in Literature from the American Academy and Institute of Arts and Letters.